One Year
Anniversary
2002

LITERARY POTPOURRI

Anthology #4

September, October, November, December
2002

Other Volumes in This Series:

#1 – Dec. 2001, Jan., Feb. 2002
#2 – Mar, Apr, May 2002
#3 – Jun., Jul., Aug., 2002

Edited by Beverly A. Jackson

Literary Potpourri is published quarterly by Lit Pot Press, Inc., PO Box 1034, Blue Lake, CA 95525. This issue is made possible in part by the generous funding of Levenger, manufacturers of fine writing/reading products, and the support of the readers and writers of Literary Potpourri ezine at http://www.literarypotpourri.com on the Internet.

Subscriptions: Send subscriptions to: Literary Potpourri, PO Box 1034, Blue Lake Ca. 95525. Single Year (4 volumes) $32.00. Single Issues $15.00.
Back Issues available.

Submissions: Send submissions to: Literary Potpourri, PO Box 1034, Blue Lake, CA 95525 or email to jacksonwrites@cox.net. Accompany all work with
SASE if sent by mail. Guidelines provided on the website.

Cover Photo © 2002 by Danny Verhasselt. "Red Dress." Reproduced with permission of the photographer. All rights reserved.

Printed by: Stride Print Services

Literary Potpourri is a trademark of Lit Pot Press

ISBN 0-9722793-3-4

LITERARY POTPOURRI

ANTHOLOGY #4

TABLE OF CONTENTS

SEPTEMBER, 2002

DECEMBER 2002

SEPTEMBER, 2002

SHORT STORIES

MY FATHER, THE BOXER

by James Simpson

It's Friday afternoon and my white-haired father is at the end of the snack aisle caressing a package of assorted tiny chocolate bars labeled "fun size." He turns the bag over in his hands and mumbles something, then says to me "These are so good." All we have in the cart so far are a box of prunes, a roll of cherry Lifesavers, a can of shaving cream, and a new toothbrush for his dentures. I have a flashback of him buying me supplies for summer camp, minus the prunes and the Barbasol.

"These small ones keep me from eating too much," he says, and I know what's coming next. "I'm still at my fighting weight of one seventy-five."

It's his weekly routine: he picks out the little chocolate bars, pats his stomach, and mentions boxing-he fought once in his life-just loud enough for anyone within earshot to hear.

I don't know why he even buys the candy; he gobbles it up on Friday night, forgets that he's eaten it, then accuses his new nurse of stealing it when she comes on Monday. Sometimes he says Mom is hiding it from him, but he broods when I remind him she died nearly ten years ago.

"Okay, Dad, let's keep moving, I have to pick up Scott at practice later."

He tosses the candy into the cart.

"Scotty still shooting the hoops, huh, good for him. Always knew he'd be a fine athlete someday, he's got natural talent."

When Scott was six or seven, my dad taught him how to shoot baskets. We hung a backboard over the garage door and they'd be out in the driveway practicing for hours. Scotty adored him, and Dad was glad to have an enthusiastic and capable pupil.

I was a clumsy kid (my oldest son, Howard, was even worse) and failed at every sport I tried. Dad was patient and encouraging, but after a while we both concluded I wasn't athletic, so we gave up. He always said it didn't matter, but seeing him with Scott I knew it did. He had waited a long time.

He was a great teacher, too; a natural athlete-agile, sharp-eyed, skillful, quick and tough. He played everything and loved competition, even tried boxing in the Navy but got knocked out in the first round of his first fight and never stepped into the ring again.

"Can't Scotty drive himself home from practice? And where's that wife of yours?"

"He's only fifteen, and I already told you Meg is showing properties this afternoon."

"Why don't you ever show properties?"

"Because I'm not in real estate. I teach math, remember?"

He looks down, picks at his sleeve like an embarrassed child.

"You never call me Pop anymore," he says softly.

Like a bolt out of the blue I don't know where this one comes from; it throws me because I've never once in my entire life called him Pop.

14

"We still have more shopping to do . . . Pop." It sounds weak and unnatural, but he smiles and we're off again.

We hit the produce section and I choose the greenest bananas I can find because I know they might sit untouched on his kitchen counter all week. He's busy fondling an apple.

"Put it back, Dad. We'll get applesauce if you want it." He frowns.

This is our last shopping trip together. Next week he'll be a resident of Belle Plantation Assisted Living Community. It sounded wonderful and regal when his doctor mentioned it in his list of the top five in the city. I pictured a stately Georgian mansion surrounded by huge moss-covered oaks, vast rolling hills and fields of wildflowers where everyone is free to roam for hours or sit on wide porches drinking sweet tea and admiring the pink azalea blossoms. In person, however, it looks more like an elementary school. I'm not thrilled about my father living there for the rest of his life, but his days of self-sufficiency are behind him.

After work one day last month I stopped by his apartment and found him stuck under the bed holding an armload of dirty clothes. He said he was looking for the laundry chute, but I reminded him that he lives on the ground floor, and the only laundry chute we ever had was in the house we lived in when I was eight.

Another afternoon he was lying prostrate on the living room floor and I swear I thought he was dead. He said he had been doing sit-ups and had lodged his feet under the couch and couldn't free himself, so he took a nap. And last week when Meg and I dropped in after breakfast he was trying to cram dollar bills and silverware into the circuit breaker box in the hallway.

15

He thought it was the safe, but of course he doesn't own a safe. That's when she and I decided he needed full-time care. Later that morning I nailed the breaker box door shut and sealed it with duct tape.

Knowing this day would come eventually, Meg and I spent many nights at the kitchen table discussing the possibility of his living with us, considering ways to shuffle our lives around to accommodate him. We had it all planned. Since Howard is grown and living on the west coast, Dad could move into his old room. I would teach part time in the morning and Meg would stay with him until I got home after lunch. She works from her office in the den most days anyway and spends weekends at open houses. It would take some adjustment, but we could do it.

When we pitched the idea to him he succinctly refused.

I don't want to cramp your style, son, was his response.

He floored me, because I'm sure he thinks-and has always thought-I don't have much style for the cramping.

* * *

We're at the orange juice section and he stands a bit stoop-shouldered, squinting at the cartons, the harsh fluorescent light bouncing off his face, making his hair glow. He resembles a turtle with his wrinkly neck stretched out, investigating.

"How many damned kinds of orange juice do they need to make now? 'Some pulp,' 'extra pulp', where's the plain old OJ?" Another ritual, the juice conundrum.

"On the bottom shelf again; not to worry."

"So where's that wife of yours these days?"

"You know how the real estate business is, she's always running around."

"She's a good little runner, too. A shame you never run with her, it'd do you good to get more exercise."

"You're probably right," I say. Meg wouldn't run if you held a gun to her head.

When had he gotten so bad? It started gradually enough with old family stories he'd told for years at holidays, but with each passing year spun more frequently with missing details, forgotten names, or with different endings. If he and I were the type of father and son who hang around together on the weekends watching hockey and drinking beer, his deterioration might not be such a shock, or maybe I could have seen it coming. Truth is we never spent that much time together until recently. Hell, even though we live in the same city, we would go for months without ever seeing each other, and we were fine with that.

Within the past year, though, he's called me more often, for no other reason than to say hello. I think he knew something was wrong and he needed help, even though he was never one to ask for it.

Behind the seafood counter he spots the young clerk he likes. She's a bubbly blonde, very cute, and I catch myself straightening, pulling in my stomach.

"There's my cute Karyn!" He pronounces it CAR-in like she's told him before. Sure, this he remembers.

He wants fish-calls it brain food as always-and asks what's good today, and I wonder which one, if any, is good for Alzheimer's.

While the two of them chat it up, I tell him to stay put (like he's going to leave Karyn?) while I go over to the deli counter to get his cheese. I'm in line for about five minutes, and when I go back to get him he and Karyn are gone. I ring the bell and she appears from the back room.

"Have you seen my father? He isn't back there bothering you, is he?"

"Oh no," she giggles. "He said he had to get some energy bars. I think that's really amazing."

"That he went to get energy bars?"

"No, silly. He's running a marathon! Twenty-six miles, I think he said. That's really impressive. Aisle seven."

"Excuse me?"

"Energy bars. Aisle seven."

"Oh, right. Thanks."

I go to aisle seven and he's nowhere in sight. Six, no luck. I make a complete lap around the store and see no sign of the marathon runner anywhere. Where the hell is he? He couldn't have gotten very far, he's not that fast these days. I imagine him somewhere in the store, in a stockroom perhaps, stuck under something after a failed attempt at pushups for a group of tittering cashiers on break.

Then I spot him in the candy aisle. He's caressing another bag of something.

"Dad, I told you to stay where you were, I'd be right back! You had me looking all over the store for you."

"I forgot these." He holds up a package of Tootsie Roll lollipops.

"No more candy, put it back." I reach for the bag.

He looks me in the eye and squares his shoulders, one hand balled into a fist. "Stop talking to me like I'm your little boy, dammit, I'm your father! And I'm buying these."

"Put it back!" I grab for the lollipops and it feels like a bag of bones. He wrenches it from my hand, the bag bursts open and a spray of brightly colored Tootsie pops clatters to the floor. He jabs me in the shoulder with his left fist enough to knock me back a step. I can't remember if he's ever punched me before, but I see he's wide open, his surprised face uncovered, and if I were a fighting man I could clock him good. I frighten myself because I really want to hit him. Hard. Something primal and irrational within me wants to knock this goddamned nonsense out of him, or shake him until he's himself again. Anything is better than this. Anything.

There is a strange quiet as though all the sound around us has been suddenly sucked out of the air, and I feel eyes on us. We must look ridiculous, poised and ready, sizing each other up for our absurd candy bout, and I start laughing, and he starts laughing, too.

"Really," he says, relaxed, smiling now, "they're not for me, they're for you."

"But I don't want them."

We kneel together and pick up the candy from the floor.

"I remember when you were young-no more than four

or five. We'd hop in my old Chevy and go to the drug store on Friday nights. You'd be standing in the front seat, or sometimes I'd let you sit in my lap-back before all this safety crap-and then we'd go into the store and I'd buy my pipe tobacco and one of these for you."

Seeing the lollipops spread out before me brings it back, and I can almost smell his pipe smoke, soft, gentle and warm. Reassuring.

"You used to love that," he says.

"And we wore matching Bermuda shorts, and those Madras shirts."

"You remember!"

It's getting late so we stuff the candy into the bag and I shove it back on the shelf. We continue down the aisle, but I turn back, grab a fresh bag and lay it in the cart.

* * *

We drive to his apartment sucking our lollipops. He asks me if I'm ever going to get married. I don't answer; I just glance at him sitting there, the muscles and tendons above his jaw working the sucker. His pudgy little body that was once so tough, so agile, is now shapeless and frail. He seems to think he's in great shape, but I wonder if he's ever frustrated or feels betrayed by his body and his mind. What must he think?

"I bought a six pack of beer," I say, "if you want to watch a Blues game or something." I'm not even sure if it's still hockey season. I don't even like hockey. It's spring, so baseball just started, that much I know.

"Sure," he says. "Blues don't play until tonight. The Cards are playing the Cubs in Chicago, though. Should still be on."

"We need to go to a game the next time they're in town." I try to sell it. "Okay, if you want." He shoots me an odd look. My unconvincing tone gives me away. "Didn't think you were much of a fan."

"Baseball's good." I don't follow sports, but it's about the only game I care to watch at all. The stats, batting averages, ERAs and scoring- basic math, sure, but interesting.

We enter his apartment and put away the groceries. He plops down in his recliner, I take the couch, and we quietly sip our beers and watch a scoreless game.

"Can I drink beer," he says flatly. I'm not sure if it's a question or an affirmation: Can I drink beer or what, buddy boy!

"You're drinking it now, Dad."

"At the new place." He's either agitated or tired, I can't decide which. "Can I drink beer at this new place I'm going to?"

"I don't think they allow it, but maybe we could sneak some in."

He nods and sets his half-empty bottle on the end table.

We watch through three innings until Sammy Sosa hits a long shot that looks like it might be a homer, but our center fielder grabs it at the warning track to end the inning. Dad doesn't react either way, and I look over and his eyes are closed, his round little belly rising up and down rhythmically, and I realize I'm running late to pick up Scott at school. I leave the game on, and before

I head out the door I stop in the hallway to check the breaker box. It's still taped shut, secure.

* * *

I call him every day at lunch and drop by after work. He's quiet and distracted, acts like he's in a rush to get me out. By Thursday he even asks me "Why are you here so often? Are you moving in or something?"

"No. Do you want to move in with us?"

He flashes a small grin, but shakes his head no. He's forgotten to shave again and his shirt is inside out.

"Tomorrow's the big day, Dad. Meg and I are taking you to Belle Plantation." God, it sounds so awful, like we're going to bury him, plant him in the ground.

"Remember, I like the light beer. Keeps my weight down. You'll sneak it in, right?"

"I'll try." We both smile broadly and laugh, but I laugh so loud and hard my eyes start to water. I reach for the kitchen towel hanging from the refrigerator door handle and wipe them. His cologne is on the towel; very faint, though, a slight lingering whiff in my nose, then it's gone.

I call Meg and tell her I'll be late, and I stick two frozen dinners in the microwave for us. Turkey, mashed potatoes and vegetables, a quickie Thanksgiving. He looks down at his plate, his hands together hovering in the air under his chin and he begins mumbling something. Is he praying? He's never been religious, so is this something new? I watch him and determine he can't decide whether to use his fork or spoon.

After dinner we watch another ballgame and he drifts

off again. While he's asleep I go into his room and set out his clothes for tomorrow and pack all the things he'll take with him. A box for his books and magazines, one for photos of us and Mom to hang on the wall, and the biggest one for his medals and trophies. I've forgotten he had so many, but there's one for each sport: tennis, golf, basketball, football, baseball, but none for boxing. Framed shadowboxes with medals and ribbons encased under glass, some as far back as grade school.

I go back into the living room and wake him gently. The game long over, a perky woman is telling us about tomorrow's weather, partly cloudy with lots of sunshine, she beams. A wonderful day.

I help him into his pajamas and he slides into bed. Before I turn out the lights he spots the boxes in the corner.

So, you packed all my medals? I've got everything I'll need?" His voice is thin and hopeful, almost pleading.

Sure did.

You didn't forget the boxing ones? He smiles up at me, but his eyes are wily.

I didn't forget. I grasp his leathery hand. "You were really good."

§ § §

James Simpson is a writer and graphic artist in Atlanta, Georgia. His fiction has appeared in Big City Lit, and StorySouth. He is currently working on a novel, but who isn't?

THE SERPENTINE JASMINE OF THE CURSED

by Hareendran Kallinkeel

"Kanyakakku sarpa dosham kanunnu," the astrologer passed his verdict.

The maiden had the curse of serpents.

Malini sat, allowed the impact of the seer's words to sink in.

Oh! The dusky skin on her thighs, the pale-brown hair on them. The slithery movement of the snakes tickled. Sometimes her hairs got tangled on their rough scales.

When she slept, they glided in sleek dancing motion between the threads of her dreams. Sometimes the cold touch of their forked tongues woke her to reality.

When she bathed, they snaked out from the shower, pounced on her in thin streaks, and dazzled her breasts with cold shivers. Sometimes they released a trickle of warmth between her legs.

They played along, all the while, just to slap her with curses?

No, the seer was wrong. Somewhere in the intricacies in calculating the position of planets, he had faltered.

She remembered the jasmine garlands. Small, white jasmines stacked in long coils. White serpents. Fragrant reptiles.

During the night, their heady smell wafting down from

25

upstairs lulled her to sleep. In the mornings she saw them in the dustbins that the maids brought from upstairs. Their brightness dead. Their fragrance smothered. Brown stains encroached their white pallor.

It was those flowers that cursed her. Not the serpents. No. Not those lovely, lively creatures.

"Aren't you listening?"

An old fang pierced; her eardrums ruptured. It hurt. "Huh?"

The baldhead came into focus. Grey eyes behind the lenses magnified. The tips of the white moustache quivered.

"Yes, daddy. I am..."

"There is a hitch in her marriage. Something unpleasant is to occur on her marriage night. She must do the *Naga Puja* in the *Sarpakkavu,* the temple of the snakes, for forty days to overcome this curse," the astrologer said.

The grey stubs became more visible on the chubby cheeks as betel leaves and areca nut grinded between the jaws. The gold rings on daddy's ears jumped as the bald head nodded in assent. "Carry on..." he said.

"This, her nineteenth year, is a crucial age. The stars say this stage determines the direction of her life. So the rituals are very important," the astrologer offered.

"But..." Malini stopped as she began. The cold wave of a look from her father froze her to silence.

The astrologer resumed, "The stars indicate marriage before twenty. But we will have to remove the *Sarpa*

Dosham , the curse of the serpents, with prayers and offerings to the *Naga Raja,* the King of the Snakes."

"What else do the stars say?" The father asked.

"Everything will be fine. Just take care of the rituals. That will avert any mishap on her wedding night." The astrologer concluded.

He gathered his *kavadi,* small shells used in calculating the position of the stars, put them in a cloth bag and tied a lace around it.

Raman counted out four five-hundred rupee notes and handed them over to the astrologer. Malini saw an eager smile light up his face as the astrologer accepted the notes. It should be ten times of what he received from an ordinary customer.

Her father tried to get her destiny weighed with willing accuracy.

The astrologer left. Raman spat out a lump of betel leaves and nuts onto the lawn. Narrow red lines appeared on the corners of his mouth. He wiped them with the back of his hand.

"You've started forgetting your manners. How often need I tell you not to interfere when men talk?"

Her father referred to her protest when the astrologer spread the shells of her destiny.

"I'm sorry, dad," Malini said.

'Oh! The wretchedness that seeps down my legs,' she thought.

"Tell me now. What did you want to say?" Her father

asked.

"My studies...I won't be able to adhere to the requirements of those elaborate rituals. It'll disrupt my studies."

"To hell with your studies. Destiny matters. Now is your time for marriage; not after your hair turns grey."

"Dad, I'm only nineteen. Can't we wait till I graduate?"

"Bullshit. Remember, you have a dent in your destiny. You have to mend it. And what should you study for? You don't need a job to support yourself." Raman spat out the remainder of beetle and nuts.

Malini stood up. The wretchedness now flowed down her legs. She started for the bathroom.

"I have amassed enough wealth for generations." Raman called after her.

'And more sins than the generations could ever hope to seek penance for.' Malini thought as she slid behind the bathroom doors.

***

The stench of scotch arrived first. The male scent of her brother.

His tall figure loomed over her study table; the dark shadow covered the monitor.

"You'll spend the rest of your life painting these stupid pictures on this screen. Why can't you do something worthwhile?" Ravi asked.

Perspiration struggled to break loose on her skin. Malini willed them back.

She did not want her brother to smell her female scent.

"I just don't understand why you are so indifferent," her brother said.

"I am sorry. I will try to mend." Malini replied.

"I doubt it. Well, tell the maids to keep ready all the four bedrooms upstairs. The houseboats and outhouses are full today. I have more tourists than I can handle."

Ravi left. The male scent remained.

Backwaters flooded with boats. Boats overloaded with foreign tourists. More tourists to flood the bedrooms upstairs. More jasmines than the maids could handle.

White jasmines illuminated the dark void around her. Her father stood there, his shadow spread a black cover over the brightness of the jasmines. Her brother approached, his shadow swallowed her father's shadow.

Her father raised his arm and patted his son on the shoulder, "Well done, my boy. You'll keep adding to my empire. You are a fine boatman who knows how to move his oars. You are a fisherman who knows where to lay the baits and when to lay them. You know how to haul the catch."

The shadow of her brother loomed larger and larger as the jasmines whimpered. The shadow moved closer to her, poised to sweep over.

The cold touch of a forked tongue woke her up from her reverie. It licked its way down her legs.

As it crept further down, she felt its warmth.

She moved. She must take care of things. She should hurry.

***

Malini heard steps on the staircase. Rapid. Heavy.

The smell of jasmines, coiled around her hair, braided in long curls, propelled her forth as Malini stepped out of the bathroom.

She walked through the bedroom and out of its door. Stunned whistles of appreciation followed her.

She stepped into the next bedroom. Shocked emission of choked breath erupted as a girl withdrew her head from Raman's lap, in answer to Malini's footsteps.

Heads turned, limbs ceased movement, as Malini treaded the third bedroom.

Amidst the suffocating male odors in the fourth bedroom, the male smell of Ravi was distinct. She stepped in, the impression of her feet silent on the floor.

Malini went straight to the dressing table. She stood for a moment in front of a portrait, eyes closed in prayer.

"Mom, why didn't you let them know your eyes were open, you could see?"

Her question cut through the sounds of passion.

Ravi stopped pumping.

Feet, soft as cotton pads, clamored the floor as the girls ran for their clothes. Girls with jasmine garlands coiled around their braids.

The scent of jasmines that churned out lust. Jasmines that brides wore on their hair on their first nights.

Rough hands pulled up trousers heaped around their feet as the tourists heard her.

Malini didn't bother to count the numbers.

She walked straight to her brother. "My body is still young. Sell it like you sell the others."

Ravi closed his eyes against the fierce glow of his sister's naked skin. His hands shot up covering his ears.

Malini stepped closer. She wrenched his hands away from his ears.

Serpents hissed. Their shining bodies wriggled in the heat of excitement. Malini felt the perspiration break loose on her glistening skin.

"Those girls you sell to these tourists are also someone's sisters. Someone's daughters."

Malini saw her brother choke. Her shadow swallowed him.

As the girls ran out of the door, Malini realized that the room filled with a suffocating haze.

Oh! Her feminine odor.

The trickle between her legs had stopped.

§ § §

Hareendran Kallinkeel is from Kerala (India), presently living in New Delhi. Hari enjoys writing, owes it to his tolerant wife and sweet little daughter.

He remembers the lush paddy fields and the hillocks beyond, listens to his grandmother's voice. His stories are appearing in the October 2002 issue of Poet's Canvas (Web) and Peeks & Valleys (print).

BROKEN BISCUITS

by Bunny Goodjohn

Tessa slung her satchel into the corner of the kitchen and headed straight for the pantry. She pulled a loaf of soft white bread from the breadbox, slavered it thickly with butter, and headed for the hallway, calling to her horse softly under her breath.

"Whisper! Whisper, come on boy!" Tessa kept her horse in the space below the stairs, among the musty folds of winter coats and spidery-Wellington boots. The horse emerged from between the chiffon scarves, handbags and raincoats and stood impatiently pawing the carpet. As Tessa bent down to adjust his girth, she blanched. The horse had chewed at her father's jacket. Neat strips of gray worsted dotted the carpet. She bent down and stuffed them in her cardigan pocket. She hoped he wouldn't notice. There'd be hell to pay.

She heard the flush of the upstairs toilet. Odd, she thought. Mother wasn't due home for at least an hour. Seconds hung as she waited. She heard the sound of running water, and then the door groaned open, framing her father. He smiled his thin grin as he loped down the stairs.

"Your Dad got a half-day! Ted got pissed at lunchtime, so they shut up early."

Whisper backed silently toward the closet door. He never let himself be seen by the others. How was school, Princess?"

Mindful of the damaged jacket, Tessa chewed at her bottom lip, playing the toe of her shoe into the carpet.

"Cat got your tongue?" He laughed and reached out his hand, a hand hard from years of fixing lawnmowers and tractors. His fingers, grimed and callused, snaked around her neck, played lightly with her braided mousy hair. He hunkered down, so their eyes were level. "You not talking to your old Dad today?"

She forced a smile. "Of course, Daddy. Everything's good. I just want to go out and play. Can I? Please?"

He turned his head to one side. "Well, I did want your help with something, but it can wait. Go on, go play before I change my mind."

Humming, her father ambled through to the kitchen in search of a beer and the remote control. She listened to him banging around in the fridge and then heard the TV, a muffled horse race from Doncaster. Whisper emerged from the duffel coats and nuzzled her arm. Quickly, she led him through the front door and down the polished steps. Looping the reins through the forsythia at the end of the pathway, she checked his bridle. The day, still eye-slantingly bright, reached out forever.

She clicked her tongue against the roof of her mouth and flicked the reins, urging Whisper into a canter. Over the shimmering tarmac, they hit the grass at full pelt. Tessa held Whisper back as they rounded the rose bushes. He had a tendency to get in front of himself, and she needed him to make it all the way to the bakery and back. They raced through the church grounds, shot over toppled gravestones, Whisper's hooves spraying marble shards. She allowed Whisper his full head as they passed the pub and screamed to a halt outside the telephone kiosk next door to the Bakery. No one was making a call, so she stabled Whisper inside the box. Brushing down her dress, she walked into the thick warmth of the baker's. Mrs. Creasey stood behind the

counter, a thick cotton apron straining to control her
ample bosom, brass curls plastered wetly to her
forehead. She wedged a crusty cob loaf into a white
paper bag, looked up and signaled that she wouldn't be
long. Tessa scanned the bakery window. Loaves of
bread, poppy seeded, glazed and still steaming, were
stacked orderly on glass shelves. Wasps throbbed
ecstatic on iced buns, feet clad in sugar. A Cabbage
White, wedged between a display of cream-filled choux
and the windowpane, beat her ragged wings.

"So, dear? What will it be today?

"Just a pound of biscuits, Mrs. Creasey. The broken
ones, please."

"You and your biscuits!"

Mrs. Creasey reached down and retrieved a battered old
tin. She tilted it into the measuring scales, and a stream
of biscuits poured into the dish: crumbling Custard
Creams, flattened Garibaldis and bottomless Jammy
Dodgers. Mrs. Creasey emptied the biscuits into a bag
and handed them to Tessa who thanked her and left the
shop. The doorbell chimed behind her and looking
back, she could see Mrs. Creasey hang the "Closed"
sign in the window. No one had occupied the phone
kiosk. Whisper brayed noisily and bared his teeth, as
she adjusted his bridle. Tessa decided to walk him
home, the heat of the pavement throbbing through the
soles of her tennis shoes.

The walk didn't calm him down. He balked at returning
to the space beneath the stairs, pawed the carpet with
his hooves and nibbled the ribs of her mother's
umbrella with his neat yellow teeth. Tessa decided it
would be safer to stable him upstairs for the night and
led him up to her room. She tied his reins to the hook
on the back of the door and placed the bag of biscuits

at the back of her wardrobe.

She knelt on the pillows at the head of her bed and gazed out across the back garden. The beds were neatly tended, gardening being one of the things her father enjoyed. He liked things just so. No weed dared to linger long within his flowerbeds. If they did, he would poison them, dig them out by the roots and toss them onto the compost heap to dry and die. Some hid deep in the beds of Nasturtiums and Snapdragons, but eventually he found them. He was a meticulous and thorough man. Tessa hated the garden. It was the reason he hadn't let her keep the puppy she found last year. He told her that puppies and gardens didn't go together.

She still yearned for a pet, something she could look after and protect. Whisper helped, but Tessa wasn't sure how long he would be around. The horse was becoming more and more unruly, less vulnerable. She tried to control him, but he was so strong. He'd taken to crapping in her mother's wicker shopping basket and chewing her chiffon scarves into tiny pieces. Lately, she'd found it hard to rein him in. She knew if she gave him his head, he'd just pound on down through the village, onto the dual carriageway, toss her off and he'd never find his way home again. Shredding the sleeve of her father's jacket was the last straw, and she knew that Whisper would have to move on soon.

Tessa watched dark birds gather on the telegraph lines, strung out like beads on a wire above the trees. Back and forth, they flew, calling out to each other like raucous kids in a playground. She watched the way the late sun lit the symmetry of their smooth bodies, the way their effortless flight was punctuated by a scramble of wings as they sought out the low thermals. The cleanness of their life appealed to her.

Her thoughts were interrupted by the sound of a key in the front door and then her mother moving about in the kitchen below. Twenty minutes later, the microwave pinged, and Tessa headed for the dining room.

"Where's Dad?" she asked over a pale imitation of Hawaiian Chicken.

From behind the TV guide, her mother mumbled, "Where he always is. Up the bloody pub." She put the magazine down beside her plate and asked, "School OK?"

"Fine, I s'pose." Tessa replied, rooting about on her plate for pineapple.

Her mother picked up the guide again. "What's your plan for this evening then?"

"I was going to go out later, down to the woods, if that's OK?"

"Fine," her mother replied, as she fumbled with the remote control, tuning out Tessa and tuning in the Australian soap.

Tessa slipped down from the table and carried her plate into the kitchen. Quietly, so as not to disturb her mother's soap opera, she eased open the pantry door, took out a sieve and pulled a chunk of bread from the loaf in the breadbox. She slipped out the back door and ran lightly down past the shed. She pushed open the squealing gate at the bottom of the garden and waded through the long whippy grass until she reached the woods beyond.

She sat down behind the large oak tree and removed a length of string from her pocket. After searching around, she found a sturdy stick with a fork at one end.

Squinting in the low sun, Tessa tied the string to the straight end of the piece of wood. She moved away from the shade of the tree into the dusty, used heat of early evening and positioned the stick on the grass with its forked end skyward. She balanced the rim of the sieve on the stick. Having crumbled the bread into a pile beneath the trap, she slowly walked back towards the shade of the oak, careful not to pull the string and thus topple the sieve to the grass.

Back behind the tree, she lay down to wait. The early evening sun beat down hot on her head and the heavy, leathery leaves of the oak tree crackled and pattered in the breeze. Face down on the dry grass, she traced question marks with a twig in the packed earth around the oak's roots. The heat made her drowsy and slowly, she dropped into a warm half-doze. Tessa watched the world shining red on the inside of her eyelids, her shorts and shirt hot against her skin.

The hum of whirring wings interrupted her reverie. She opened her eyes and peered out from behind the trunk. Beneath the propped sieve, a glossy, plump blackbird pecked indifferently at the breadcrumbs. The bird wasn't black, but iridescent blue-black. His beak shone gold against his feathers, and between every peck, he checked around with wary, watching eyes. Tessa made sure she had tight hold of the string and, in the time it takes to tell a lie, jerked her hand back. In a flurry of feathers, squawks and breadcrumbs, the stick whipped away, toppling the sieve and imprisoning the bird.

She watched the bird. It ran blindly in tight, sieve-sized circles, tried with frantic wings to lift the metal meshed cage. She tried to calm the bird, talking to it in her quiet little girl's voice until the bird ran out of power and slumped in the grass. Gently, with shaking fingers, Tessa lifted the sieve an inch and curled her damp hand around the bird, holding it firm. She was immediately aware of its fine bones, hard and thin beneath its chest feathers. Lifting the black bird to her face, she looked into its eyes. It breathed in ragged, hot little bursts, its heart jack hammering against her palm. Its eyes darted from side to side, then closed, its quaking bird-body trembling in her hand. Tessa recognized that closed-eyes resignation. She buried her nose in its dusty feathers and inhaled. She smelt its fear, could taste it, smoky on her tongue. Smoky like Daddy's mouth-taste when he got into her bed and kissed her and when he whispered be good, and don't cry and don't tell Mummy.

She raised her clasped hands over her head and with a triumphant yell, threw the bird up into the sky. As it wheeled and soared higher and higher into the air, Tessa took the yell and hid it deep in her heart. The bird looped back to the telegraph wire and was lost in the roosting string. The early evening was giving way to dusk and Tessa walked slowly back, past the oak, up the garden path, past her father's shed, through the back door and up the stairs to her bedroom. It was Friday night, and there were biscuits to eat before Daddy came home.

§ § §

Bunny Goodjohn, originally from the UK, now resides in Forest, Virginia and is a junior at Randolph Macon Woman's College.

Her poetry has appeared in the literary journal, Concrete Wolf and in the magazines, Mélange and Wind. In 2001, she was awarded Honorable Mentions in both the Helen Calvert Award and the Don Goodwin poetry competition.

When she isn't writing (which is rare,) Bunny enjoys growing veggies in the back garden, emailing friends back in Blighty and cooking up a vegetarian storm in the kitchen.

FLASH FICTION

THE CURSOR

by Gary Presley

The cursor blinks. Perhaps I should change the screen background color. White is paper-like, but my old word processor sported a sky blue with a white font. Is that it? I miss the blue.

The cursor blinks. Five thousand words await assembly for an article describing how wavelike properties dominate the behavior of electrons. Two thousand words delay converging to describe antiretroviral therapy.

The screen glows. My bulldog snores gently in the corner. I click on the Internet browser. Dare I? A new identity can be woven quickly from the World Wide Web. A birth certificate, a Social Security card, a new driver's license. The right paper stock. A laser jet printer. A digital camera. Too easy. Next a credit history. I am a writer. Creative nonfiction.

The loan officer smiles politely and pushes the note across her desk. Her children watch from silver frames and Dilbert stares blankly from the side of a coffee cup. I sign.

And then I sign again. The salesman grins greedily, his pinky ring flickering in the light of a fat commission. He tosses me the keys to a blood-red Dodge Viper.

I set that bad boy loose on the open road. I carry only plastic, clothes I can buy when I get to Miami. I drive all night, the headlamps burning a hole out of my past. I chase aspirin with coffee, hot and black, and eat chocolate for energy. It is 23 hours to the city of tropical promises, and I will not be denied. I intend to hook up with a hot-blooded Cubana emigré and eat salsa in a funky outdoor cafe.

Electrons can fend for themselves.

She is dark and slender, with a faint scar above her right eyebrow, and never wears a bra. She eats eggs and rice and sausage in the morning and begins her daily ration of twelve Cuba Libres at noon. Maria Elena Guiterriz sucks the passion from my soul. Two weeks leave me too weak. Too hot not to burn down, such an affair. I tire of screams and broken crockery. I quail when knives flash and there is talk of guns.

I toss jeans and t-shirts in a gym bag and cram it in the Viper's trunk. I smell New Orleans in the wind. I stop mid-trip to sniff out my destiny. I am in the bright bar of a casino in Biloxi. The bartender smiles while I sip a straight shot of Maker's Mark. I sense her aura. A woman at peace with fate. I decide to dip into her mojo. I lift $5 from her tip jar and slink off to the blackjack tables. In two hours I parlay that pittance into more money than I could accumulate in a decade of freelancing.

I decide I will live in the French Quarter and write the Great American novel.

I leave the Viper, keys in the ignition, at the edge of Jackson Square. I need it no more. I rent a walk-up apartment, one with a wrought iron balcony covered by an awning dripping with ivy and rust. My landlady is an ancient one-eyed Creole who smells of gin and old leather. I write every morning while the police scrape up drunken tourists from the gutters of Bourbon Street.

Early one Sunday I seek out café au lait and beignets at Emeril's. Bam! A stranger bumps into my chair, spilling champagne on my manuscript.

It is Julia Roberts.

She apologizes breathlessly and then reaches for the manuscript to blot up the pearls of wine. She pauses, begins to read, glancing sideways shyly once to see if I recognize her. I remain cool. I like her films, but I am angered that she trifled with Lyle Lovett's heart.

"Hmm," Julia says, offering me the incandescent smile that melts hearts and earns millions. "I've been looking for a comic novel to translate onto film. This is brilliant. Sophisticated, yet simple. Eclectic in philosophy, deeply intellectual, but not afraid to revel in the bawdiness of human foibles. Full of symbolism, for those willing to dig for it, but a rousing tale for Everyman nonetheless."

Odd. In interviews she comes across as quite dull. The woman is actually remarkably intelligent. She pauses to flip through several more pages. "May I ask your name?"

I tell her. She reaches toward me with the offer of a handshake. Her touch is electric.

I jump.

The cursor blinks. The screen is white. The bulldog snores.

§ § §

Gary Presley lives and writes in Missouri. He believes bean dip is haute cuisine, blue jeans are formal attire, and has no fantasies about writing the Great American

45

Novel unless such work followed a career as a major league baseball pitcher.

His nonfiction work has appeared in national and regional print publications and various on-line venues, including Salon.com.

THE DOGS OF PEACE

by Alan C. Baird

INT. TRIANON - LATE, LATE, LATE AT NIGHT. JUNE, 1920.

What's this? A meat hook impales the familiar red/white/green shape of a certain Eastern European country, Austria's unwilling wartime partner. The supporting cable contains a weight-scale meter which reads 100.

An officious little functionary with a huge nose approaches the meat hook. He's brandishing a much-too-big cutlass, and obviously fancies himself quite the swordsman. As he delicately slices a small piece from the red/white/green map's left side, its weight-scale now indicates 98, and a tiny drop of red liquid runs down the side of the meat-hook-impaled map.

The functionary grabs the portion he's carved off, and throws it over to a slavering dog, who waits in the shadows. The pooch is oddly colored - red/white/red, top-to-bottom.

The functionary is now beginning to enjoy his bloody little task, and steps up to the map with relish. As he severs a sizable chunk from the top, his weight-scale shows 79, and the red liquid flows down freely, all over the map. He tosses this newest filet negligently over to several smaller dogs, who wait hungrily in another dark corner.

SLASH! Another incision appears near the map's bottom, and the weight-scale hovers near 60. An unruly pack of canines begins to fight over this wedge. Blood spurts all over them.

One last gash butchers a huge area from the right side, dropping the weight-scale below 29. The functionary is now smeared with red, and he's grinning fiendishly, as he hands over the territory to a pit bull. This dog is also colored strangely: blue head, yellow midsection, and red hindquarters.

FADE TO BLACK.

[Afterword: Over 70% of one country "vanished" in The Great War. Today, the exiles' great-great-great-grandkids still think in Magyar.]

Editor's note: Few nations in contemporary history have been struck by a calamity of such lasting impact as Hungary when, on June 4, 1920, as a consequence of the peace treaty of Trianon, she was deprived of her historical boundaries and two-thirds of her territory and population, including 3,400,000 Hungarians attached to the neighboring states. At the same time, Germany lost but 13.5 percent of its former lands to victorious neighbors, and Bulgaria a mere 8 percent. Thus, the greatest injustice in Paris was committed against Hungary, as if that country were mainly to blame for the war and its outbreak.

§ § §

Alan is the Harvard Book Prize winner who recently coauthored "9TimeZones.com" - a hardback/softcover/web/wap project featured in the Whitney Biennial. He lives just a stone's throw away from Hollywood..which is fine and dandy, until the stones are thrown back.

CAIN

by Avital Gad-Cykman

The day I returned from the summer camp, my brother left home. He waved at me from the bus and shouted: "Jake, you're the man of the house now!"

My crying father and dumbstruck mother measured me up.

"Hey, he's eighteen and it's time he lived on his own," I said.

They went up to his empty room. I said, "He'll return happier and healthier, perhaps engaged. Maybe he'll have a mortgage of his own."

"We miss him so much," they said.

I slammed their plates on the table. I said, "I am trying hard."

They tasted the soup I had made for dinner. "Is it good?" I asked.

They lowered their eyes.

§ § §

Originally from Israel, Avital Gad-Cykman has lived in Brazil for the past twelve years. She has published her stories in publications she still admires. When she doesn't write she sees it is almost springtime where she lives.

PHOTO ESSAY

FIESTA DEL CORAZON

by James Tynes

1

James Tynes is a freelance writer and self-taught artist living in Austin, Texas. He's a graduate of the University of Texas, Austin. He's worked in Mexico with autistic children, and traveled in Guatemala

POETRY

SAUGUS, EMBASSY OF THE SECOND MUSE

by Tom Sheehan

He has come out of a dread silence and given himself a name; Saugus, he says.

He bleats like a tethered goat to come out of that coming, to be away, dense spiral to the core of self, to the mountain call, bird arc across such slopes of pale imaginings. Saugus, he says: I am that part of you cries not for the love but intimacy of words, light touch of skin we dread and seek, owning up of self as if in another. I am that part of you named endless searcher, thirsty one, guzzler, sufferer, warred on, the starved and the wasted, that part of you you can't turn over by yourself. I have the secrets you do not know you know. I am lodged in a far corner of mind, some fallow place at reins' end, waiting to be routed out, turned up, to green a page again. Has it taken you so long to find me, or do you ignore me and try it on your own? You cannot avoid documented lightning, shock of metaphor, God on one knee, Saugus. I am not a stranger. I breathe with you, find shelter and warmth when you do, know the single star haunting the edge of your horizon, know best of all the magic when the sound is right. Oh, Thomas! when the sound is the music of one word upon another, and it tears two parts of soul to four because nothing like it has been heard before, when the word dances on its consonants, slides on abducent vowels, when the spine knows the word is known by every ganglia, thong and sinew of the body. The coring.

I am Saugus and you waste me away, cast me aside. I who carry all sounds of memory, cast me aside at breast-panning, when you lose the music down in some phantom crotch, when a sweet ass ties your brain in knots. Now, just now, Thomas, feel the core wind in. Feel the word rock in you. Find the word rock. Chip at it. Let the chisel fly, the sparks dance out globally, the word broken away from the granite source in you. Don't you know me, Thomas? I am the gate tender. I am the one who lets you find the word rock. I am the keyman. I let you into that vast field of yourself where the rock grows. I am Saugus, and I tend that field where the rock lies in the sacred cairn. We meet so infrequently. I keep myself here waiting on you, the gate eager to rise, the field waiting to know your tread, the rock waiting to be beat upon by the hammer of your desire. I am lonely when you wander. It is dark and fearful without you. And yet I can make you cry when I am lonely. You don't believe me yet...I am Saugus who makes you cry.

You can't tease me, please me, appease me. Just use me. I am servant of servants. I am Id's Id's Id, ego sans ego sans ego. I am to be used, exploited, submitted.

And I guard that huge rock in you, tend it, know what filled it dense as hardpan that time in Boxford field and you hurt all over; dense as the frozen earth DeMatteo dug fox holes with C-3 and it finally blew off the back of his head and Colonel Mason said, "Shit!"; dense as Vinegar Hill or Indian Rock or that rock wall outside Schenectady and you stopped to change a tire at her waving and she slid down that wall at her back motioning to you her bodily gratitude. Dense is that word rock, full of all your lore and legend bricked with every movement you've ever known, all sights and sounds and music of the words; that special place where the thing rings in you, that place of core vibration.

Jesus, Thomas, take my hand again! Walk in the field with me. We belong together, you and I. Dispel me of doom. Let the music of words come, let them dance first in your eye, roll on your tongue, live to die on the page. Let them vibrate on your spine, get kissed of your skin, shoot out of here in flight of geese, and mournful sound of heading home when there is no home, steaming freight train whistle calling you from a circle of blue nights, self shout at the moon still shining on a hill East of Cleveland, South of Yang-du, East again a long stretch from the Chugach given you in a word picture, West of a cliff near Kerry and rain moved as a god laughing at the rootstock of your silence, Celtic mummery, God buried in stone. If you can't come with me, Thomas, you are the loser, lonely, forsaken. I can take you back to all the hard places, to the adjectives and verb ends; to the quadrangle in Japan in 1951 and the cool wind coming through Camp Drake and the voice of death talking in it and calling Maciag's name (Body Hunger) and little Salazar (Arab Dagger) and Captain Kay (Memphis Peon) and Billy Pigg (Cowpoke) and Stoney Mason (Pennsy Slateman) and Anadazio (Bread You Can't Imagine) and Dan Bertelsen (AKA The Knife) and you listened and it didn't talk your name and you still felt sad and knew you were the only ear. In three weeks they were gone, all gone, and their voices went into ground, and all their words, and they built on the word rock and now they still dance sadly...such words that make you cry with music still in them, and they come long and slowly out of another time funnel, like Billy Pigg saying, "Shit" as he rolled over in your arms and Captain Kay saying, "I just want to go home for a little while and tell Merle and Andy I love them. Just for an hour or so." Do you remember, then, later, far from the Land of the Morning Calm, the room in Ireland, that space of pewter walls, made hard by the anvil?...The spark spray of peacock's fire, head-tucked-under-wing smell ripe as working acids, dead melons; tin-plated, throat-sucking water weaving its skin of iron dust thick as magnetized talcum; the unknown and unsure shapes of heat, cool in its third form, introducing friction to mattered air, the sound a gulping sizzle that swallowed bar, froze form, and the voice of the man at the end of the hammer and the end of your poem, saying, "That poem, my man, is iron. You made a good pour, a good draw. You beat it well. It's iron." And all the words come out of ground, out of rock, erupt and blow at you.

I am Saugus. I can make you cry. I remember more than you the sound of silence just before the word breaks. I am the edge of all things, the point of it all, Saugus.

§ § §

Eleven years retired, Tom Sheehan operates with his partner, Larry Bucaria, Newwriters.com, helping writers find publishing space.

He has work in Paumanok Review, 3amMagazine, Small Spiral Notebook, Dakota House, Stirring, Samsara,

Comrades, Split Shot, Melange, Red River, Nefarious, Carnelian, New Works Review, Eclectica, Slow Trains, Clackamas Review, etc.

A print novel, "Vigilantes East," has just been released by Publish America, and another, "An Accountable Death," is serialized on 3amMagazine.

He has been nominated for Pushcart Prize XXVII and awarded a 2001 Silver Rose Award for Excellence in the Art of the Short Story by American Renaissance for the Twenty-first Century (ART).

This poem is from a poetry manuscript, "This Rare Earth and Other Flights," of which more than 50 poems have appeared in print or on electronic sites.

GOOD CONVERSATION

by Valerie Witte

Little Blue told me, while skewering
scallions and piercing red peppers,
that he would marry a 400-pound woman.
If she smothered him, pushing
out air through lips and nostrils; flattened
him like skin, or if he, lacking direction,
were unable to navigate her
streams and straits, caverns
and coves; if he became lost in her
vast expanse,
it wouldn't matter, he said, flipping
kabobs, bathing them in Kansas City
Masterpiece. As long as she made
good conversation.

§ § §

Valerie Witte holds a BA in English writing from Rhodes College. Her writing has appeared in The Southwestern Review and the chapbook In the Margins. She currently works in the electronic production department at a medical publishing company in St. Louis

TIDBIT FOR GOD

by Celia Homesley

Mostly I waited like a pebble on your doorstep
until night grew wan and light
gave birth to streets. Then my shoelaces
revealed themselves, dangly as worms,
a metaphor for a life undone, though I tried
to impress you with my great coat over
silver wings as if I could live
among the others, stroll along gentleman-like,
or leave this place, an angel so heavy with regret
she can hardly lift away, but she does,
and light leads her, the fierce light of day-stars,
and she rises (but you know this part) above the statues
and the glass-topped buildings; every enclosure,
even bodies sticky with grime seem vacant and clean.

§ § §

Celia Homesley holds a BA in English and Journalism from Humboldt State University and an MFA in poetry from San Francisco State University. She has been published in various literary journals including The Bloomsbury Review, The Sow's Ear Review, Fourteen Hills: The SFSU Review, and Luna. She currently lives in Arcata, California where she writes and teaches English at College of the Redwoods and Humboldt State University.

IN THE HOUR BEFORE

by Jim Boring

In the hour before freezing
The pond gathers viscosity
Sinks below a fragile glaze
Lies still beneath the glistening lace
And waits.

In the hour before dying
The woman gathers memory
Sinks below their tender gaze
Lies still beneath her crumbling face
And waits.

§ § §

*Jim Boring lives on the Illinois-Wisconsin border from
which vantage point he is able to peer into the woods
dark and deep or the city equally dark and deep. He has
published in the small press and in the Chicago Tribune
Magazine.*

ESSAY

I WENT TO BARNES, I WENT TO NOBLE

by Bob Arter

I had never been to one.

My writerly chums routinely reported that they all but dwelt in such sanctuaries, poring over the lit mags that just as routinely snubbed their efforts. I reckoned they stole time for Calvin and Hobbes, coffee and rolls and Italian juices. My friend Peggy, who writes only post cards and to-do lists, but who reads voraciously, insisted I come along with her. She was determined to further my own writing career, which had, in but a few short years, garnered me one hundred dollars and two bars of French chocolate.

Peggy had eaten the chocolate.

So many entirely disparate books and publications, I mused, pen gone to paper, plume to doom, garret agony and the giddy joy of a summer seller. Even the certifiably good writers, Shakespeare and Melville and Twain, all had to jostle for the primo shelf space with Miz Steele, with Cap'n Clancy, with the pair of imaginative fellows who had penned Molecular Biology Made Fun and Simple.

The checkout woman told me, "I never take home a paycheck." She was terribly proud of the fact. She wore some sort of apron, heavy muslin or lightweight canvas, and beneath it she resembled some aging serving wench, plump, all Henry Fielding. Do you know those porcelain characters produced in limited numbers by, oh, the Franklin Mint? Or all that Beatrix Potter crap? She looked like that, and I wished she carried a butter dish.

I thought, This woman could be my age. Conceivably,
she and I might be anticipating our twentieth
anniversary, out here in California in a house walled
with books, fruit of her employee discount. I wanted to
ask her if we would put up striped tents and awnings in
the yard, fly pennants and rent an above-the-ground
pool (earning the contempt of our neighbors, but fun
for the children while we adults spoke French, spoke
caramel apples, spoke a billion pasta noodles and
looked at one another, remembering high school and
the dead, smiling big to contain our tears).

There were blank books and talking books and
magazines filled with astrology and naked women, all
there at the counter for the impulse buyers. Another,
younger woman had previously led me, yoked as an ox
is yoked, over to the shelf of audio books. They were
chatting amiably, Frost to Tolkien to Philip K. Dick,
whose stock was soaring because of the movie deal,
and the book deal, and the yackety compact disk deal,
all being marketed together, like burgers, shakes, fries.
Imagine Philip K. Dick off on a cheeseburger chat with
Edith Hamilton, with Edith Wharton, with Edith.

Edith was a one-name poet I had earlier discovered on
the table of cut-rate merchandise this behemoth was
desperate to sell, and I was intrigued, and while giving
one ear to my aproned wife, no paycheck but plastic
dishes at the party, the madness of tents, I thought
about the sort of life I might have had with Edith. She'd
have been moody, I was certain, but pliable on
occasions, as when we ventured out to the produce
markets in Greece, in Calabria, in some Chinese Huang
Zee Broccoli, back to our junk or tiny room for an
afternoon of sex and conversation.

Her poetry was scattered like crows across the drab

newsprint skies of little folios, five or six dollars each. It was evidently inspired by a studied hatred of nature, for she carried on about the bitch birch rattling in my gust of fury and some sorely troubled wolf that savages gobbets of my gut and so on. I decided against pets-God knows what horrors she might suspect a guinea pig of contemplating-but I was betting she was plenty hot.

I felt a certain amount of guilt for thinking such treacherous thoughts in the shopwoman's chattery presence. I wondered if she were married, but couldn't glimpse her finger. She was still rambling on: ". . . and an increase by one-half of my thirty percent in the week after Christmas-don't you love that week? Of course there's the inventory, but I have family here-do you know how to make a plum pudding? In a coffee can? Oh, we have three aisles of cookbooks, Emeril to Martha to that barbecue person, and Sharon-she showed you our talking books-well, I do go on, but she found a delicious recipe in a holiday cookbook by this fascinating old man in the Blue Mountains of-"

I had located an old paper volume by Least Heat Moon, and bought it for Peggy. It wasn't chocolate, but she wasn't choosy. She kissed me, there at the counter, in that enormous emporium of words and I leaned back and I returned the kiss, and lingered, and all anniversary plans were off, the poet sent packing, and I didn't have the eleven cents in change.

§ § §

Bob Arter loves sushi but it's damnably hard to locate fresh fish in the desert and he's getting sick and tired of fossilized trilobites. He plays first base for the Dodgers, now in his 37th season. lifetime obp: .908. his rookie card is worth a buck and a half. Oh yeah, and he faces weapons charges in three nations and is even now fighting extradition. According to his attorney, Maryanne Stahl, he is a tall, handsome fellow except for the...

BOOK REVIEW

The Bush Dyslexicon by Mark Crispin Miller

Book Review by Michael J. Luyckx

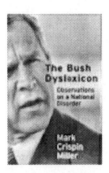

While researching "The Bush Dyslexicon," I found it listed on the whitehouse.org's inventory of terrorist reading material. Even though it's true that special agents of the FBI are visiting local libraries, checking reading logs to discover subversive elements in our society, under authorization from the Patriot Act, whitehouse.org is an initiative of Chickenhead productions and a parody on the real whitehouse.gov website. Nevertheless, it demonstrates the fame and impact of "The Bush Dyslexicon."

Knowing the reputation and hype surrounding "The Bush Dyslexicon, Observations on a National Disorder" by Mark Crispin Miller, I looked forward to working my way through the book and form my own opinion. Mr. Miller, a professor of media studies at New York University, has published numerous noteworthy writings, including in The Nation and in the New York Times and his previous book, "Boxed in: The culture of TV" is definitely worthwhile several afternoons of your time.

According to the prologue "Look who's talking", the writer admits this book is clearly "anti-Bush" (p.2) but more importantly it "is meant to shed some light on propaganda in our time. The Dyslexicon attempts to give the light to that enormous wave of propaganda - a joint production of the GOP and major media- whereby George W. Bush was forced on us as president". Mr. Miller is trying to demonstrate how the current president of the United States was not only not elected, but put in the oval office by a machinery of extreme rightist coalitions, who blatantly disregard any respect for democratic values.

The author sets out by elaborating on the Bush clan affiliations with the Nixon, and more importantly, with the Reagan administration. He demonstrates how the GOP desperately tries to copy the "hypnotic savoir-faire" of the late J.F.K. He points out that it is already apparent at that time that none of the republican candidates have the same "televisual charm" so often displayed by their counterparts from the democratic front. He describes that Nixon "looked like a neglected mental patient next to Kennedy, who seemed as hale and masterful as his opponent looked awestruck and underfed". Still according to the author, by 1988 the Bush campaign machine had finally managed to democratize his image just enough to get him into office. In addition, he points out that Bush junior, learning from his elder's mistakes, knows how to "charm a lot of voters in the Sun Belt, the farm states, the Rocky Mountain states and other strongholds of far-right Republican emotion."

Mr. Miller then elaborates on George W. Bush's education, and how he worked his way through Andover, Yale and Harvard. He extensively covers Bush's attitude of disinterest in both homeland or foreign policy and his general illiteracy. The author claims that Bush junior is more than just not good at this disinterest: when Tucker Carlson asked Bush to name something he isn't good at, Bush replied, "'Sitting down and reading a 500-page book on public policy or philosophy or something." The writer tries to demonstrate George W.'s seeming pride in not being very literate at all: "And I see Bill Buckley is here tonight, fellow Yale man. We go way back, and we have a lot in common. Bill wrote a book at Yale- I read one."

The author exposes how George W. Bush continuously shows very limited knowledge on fundamental topics or desperately tries to avoid giving direct answers when asked about Religion, Freedom of Speech, Abortion or Gay Rights. Cunningly, Bush avoids these direct answers knowing that his ideas and opinions were inspired by his elitist education and the rightist influences that have been loosely associated with the GOP since the early 70's.

We learn from the book that when asked about the Rocker incident and his opinion on the Braves' decision of getting the player counseling, Bush answered that "in America we can say what we want to say, but that doesn't mean that if the man needs help, he shouldn't' get it". Not exactly a Bushism and not exactly what one would expect from a republican who generally "deplore(s) the tendency to treat hate speech as a crime." On military and foreign policy issues, Bush shows a deplorable lack of knowledge not only of global history but also of the geo-political reality of the 21st century, calling Greeks Grecians, Timorese Timorians and mistaking Slovenia for Slovakia.

Mark Miller provides accurate documentation on those subjects the president desperately tried to evade during the campaign: his affiliations with the oil industry in Texas, his record settings in the Texan judicial system or his lack of concern for the environment. When questioned about global warming Bush replied that he doesn't "think we know the solution to global warming yet, and I don't think we've got all the facts before we make decisions". It should come to no surprise to us then that as soon as Bush was firmly seated in the oval office, the United States withdrew from the Kyoto agreement. Miller documents very well how Texas is one of the nation's biggest producers of greenhouse gasses and how the main parties responsible are those companies that have heavily sponsored the current president's campaign. Obviously Bush therefore is "trying to protect my invest- my contributors from unscrupulous practices," as he stated when asked about campaign finance reform.

It becomes apparent during the book that the reporters of all big networks failed to notice the artistic tap-dancing George W. displayed in trying to evade these questions. Using techniques previously used by his father and his mentor Nixon, he displayed an incredible aptness at passing "the message" and turning the tables on the media.

What the book fails to demonstrate is why the reporters don't, or at least pretend not to, notice this strategy. With every example of how the TV coverage lacks the investigative nature one would expect from objective newsgathering, the author misses an opportunity of exposing the ties between the GOP and the five major networks. One would expect this scrutiny from a professor in media and unfortunately this book only skims the surface of the intricacies of this alleged influence. There must be some profound reasons why the coverage of the electoral campaign was so slanted in Bush' advantage as Miller so clearly demonstrates. To my disappointment, I could not find the answer to that question in this book, and hope it is an area that Mark Miller will further examine in future publications.

The book is a very good demonstration why there should be numerous questions about how George W. Bush became the 43rd president of the United States. As the author sets forth to demonstrate that this is largely due to the propaganda machine in this time of quick indulgence and instantaneous gratification of personal desires and wants, he falls short of this noble goal: he exposes the machine, but not the inner workings of its engine. As an overview of Bush's background, education (or lack thereof), ties and influences and who the actual powers behind the throne might be, this book is excellent in its endeavors. It definitely lives up to the "Anti-Bush" image the author warned us for in the beginning and as such is food for thought and deserves it's place on the bookshelf of everyone who feigns any interest in the political landscape of the most powerful nation in the 21st century. However on the same note, I would like to advise the politically interested to read books like "Eyewitness To Power, the essence of LeaderShip Nixon to Clinton" by David Gergen or "The Presidential difference, Leadership style from Roosevelt to Clinton" by Fred I. Greenstein in order to understand and appreciate Mark Miller's book in a broader political context.

For further reading on presidential propaganda machines, I highly recommend "Spin Cycle, Inside the Clinton Propaganda Machine" by Howard Kurtz; and for a more detailed look at the role of the media in our current political climate and how much power they actually wield, "Governing With the News: The News Media As a Political Institution (Studies in Communication, Media and Public Opinion)" by Timothy E.Cook also makes excellent additional reading.

§ § §

Michael J. Luyckx is a graduate of the University of Leuven's Rega School in Belgium and an avid amateur of modern history and politics, washed ashore in Texas where he tries to provide for a family of wayward children and other people usually found under bridges and overpasses.

In his spare time he loves to monopolize the kitchen (his food concoctions are often referred to as Belgilicious), tries to enjoy theatre and read as much as he can. Only when completely exhausted by children, neighbours or any other household pests, will he absorb the relentless images of consumer society as they ooze out the television set.

MID MONTH SURPRISE

CROSS COUNTRY

by Terry DeHart

She isn't looking for trouble, and she doesn't expect trouble to be looking for her. She chants no mantra on this day. She listens to the steady bellows of her lungs and the rushing of blood in her arteries. Her feet rise and fall, heel-toe, heel-toe, and her body moves against the lycra encasement of her running tights. She's locked into her long-distance pace, which isn't blindingly fast, but she's taught herself to never quit and she could, perhaps, run down a deer if she had enough time.

She's running along the centerline of a road, but there aren't any cars. It's a closed section of highway that curves along the Oregon side of the Columbia River Gorge--a condemned two-lane blacktop made long ago for tourists in Model A Fords, but now is only cracked concrete with lines of green where the grass pushes through. She runs into narrow, dripping tunnels blasted from solid rock by the WPA, and then she runs out the other side into the living explosions of blackberry vines that close the road down to one lane, in places. She crosses short bridges with mossy stonemason walls. Lichen hangs from the trees like moistened beards. The sky is overcast, as usual, and water is everywhere. Waterfalls rush white through the fern-dark underbrush. The woman's face is wet from heavy drops falling from the trees: maple, beech, Douglas Fir, cedar, ash. Rain patters on leaves and courses down slick trunks, but the woman doesn't stop to partake of this sensual feast. She is only semi-aware of her surroundings because she's working to improve herself, improve her time. She believes the beauty of the land will still be there, when she's finished.

The Columbia River is two miles wide below her, but the woman will not drown. The river drains the land from Montana and up into British Columbia and then it rolls back to the south and then west to the sea, all the time nurturing its populations of salmon and steelhead and sturgeon. There are eels on the rocks, bass in the sloughs, ducks and geese in the wetlands. In the hills above the river there are bobcats, coyotes, foxes, and perhaps mountain lions and black bears, but wild animals do not stalk the woman. Nature surrounds her and she is young and she feels unthreatened, as she always has, in the forest.

Though her life has never been in danger, she is aware that horrible things happen. She was raised in a town surrounded by old-growth timber and so she was raised to be self-sufficient. In a small pack strapped to her back, she carries a cache of emergency supplies. The items are miniature and, on ordinary days, sufficient: waterproof matches, a tube of antiseptic lotion, tissue paper, a half-dozen Band-Aids, her wallet and keys. It's a very sensible kit for her to carry, and the small weight of it, if she thinks of it at all, makes her feel she is a pragmatic person.

She keeps her pace. There aren't any other people in sight. No fellow runners or hikers or bicyclists. It wouldn't matter to her if there were other people. Her running is a deep meditation, her mind focused inward upon itself. In this mindset, she is convinced that her lungs do not burn, the muscles of her legs do not ache, her stomach does not protest. On the straights, she closes her eyes and goes as close to a transcendental state as she dares. She catches glimpses of the people she loves: her mother's hands knitting a sweater, her father's Adam's apple bouncing up and down when he laughs, the brown eyes of the gentle boy she dated in high school.

And so it comes as a great surprise when she trips over a length of heavy fishing line pulled taut across her path. One second she's moving and the next, she's kneeling in a puddle and trying to catch her breath. Her shins burn from their impact with the line and her knees leak blood. She hears a rustling in the trees and a gloved hand snakes from the undergrowth. A strange arm lunges for her as if to save her, catches hold of her hair and then pulls her into the bushes. The pain of her fall and the pain of the man's grip flood to the fore, but she doesn't believe the pain is real. The leaves of the underbrush shake and release their burden of water as the arm pulls her along. She doesn't scream or lash out as she's heard she must, under the circumstances. The rain slips down and replaces the water falling from the leaves. A freight train enters a tunnel on the far bank of the river. The woman disappears.

The man holding her is wearing a red and green ski mask, as is the other man who strips off her running tights. Their faces are the colors of Christmas, but their eyes are hungry and mean. The abuse is worse than she might've guessed, had she only read about it in the newspaper. A stunning rain of blows, at first. No reason, no explanation, only the grunting of exertion and the flat, smacking sound of fists on flesh. She curls up and tries to go to that place in her mind that comes when she runs.

They pull off the rest of her clothes. She tries to resist, but her arms emerge from arm holes and her legs retreat from leg holes until she is naked. She feels the cold growth of moss and lichen against her skin and she wants to pull it over her like a blanket. She tries work herself into the ground, but the soil is too thin.

When she struggles beneath the first man, it isn't a savage defense, but only a sort of protesting isometric exercise beneath his weight. The man lifts from her and the second man forces himself upon her much more roughly than the first. The second man hits her until a moan comes from her bleeding lips and then he laughs. When he's finished, she tries to sit up but he pushes her back down with the sole of his boot.

The men have a short conversation, their breath steaming the air. She doesn't hear what they say. They remove their masks. The second man snaps open the blade of a small folding knife. The woman feels as if she is an animal that has been hit by a car. Her vision is blurred and the men and the forest look soft and muted as the backdrop of a dream. The second man walks toward her and it's only a few steps, but it seems to take forever.

The woman has always listened to the signals of her body, and now the signals tell her that she is in no condition to run. Her mind tries to solve the problem of it. She feels the bulge of her small pack caught between her back and the soft forest floor. The men didn't take it, but there isn't anything in it that would help her, now. She doesn't believe in violence, but she longs for a weapon. The longing comes from nowhere and everywhere and it seems slightly ridiculous to her, even under the circumstance, but the image comes anyway: Her pulling a gun from the pack, pointing and firing, and then the image is gone in its own desperate balloon of unreality.

The second man stands over her and she looks up at him and says, "Don't." The man laughs. "Little late for that, isn't it?" He comes at her and stabs her with the knife. She holds up her hands and takes a few defensive cuts to her arms and then the knife finds her once, twice, three times high in the chest, but the small blade doesn't penetrate to her vital organs. She isn't dead, but they wrap her in a blanket and lash it down with their heavy fishing line. They drag her as they might drag a rolled-up carpet. She loses consciousness.

There's no light. No water, no sky, no earth, only pain. Only suffering in the cold air. But then she hears a sound. Something is moving. Tires on pavement, swaying hell, the smell of blood. She fades in and out and then she opens her eyes as wide as she can. She moves to the limits of her bindings as waves of sickness roll from the darkness, but she fights until the dizziness subsides. She struggles again and the line comes free. It isn't necessary to tie strong knots for a dead woman, she thinks. Moving slowly, she tests her arms and legs for damage. No bones are broken but when she moves, her t-shirt sticks to the blood on her chest and the pain nearly causes her to lose consciousness again. She stops moving. She listens to her ragged breath coming in and going out and she feels the fingers of terror fluttering on her skin and then the fingers become more purposeful and start to take hold of her. She stifles an urge to scream.

The thought enters her mind that she should let the men continue to think she is dead. She cries silently. The tears drip from her face like raindrops from a muddy leaf, but no one can see her. After a few minutes she understands that tears have no power in this place. She cries until the flashes of her panic begin to grow dimmer. Gradually, she finishes with crying because it can do no more for her.

With great effort, she pushes against the fear, forces it into a corner of her mind and holds it there. She waits to make certain it won't break loose again. She squeezes her eyes shut and takes a smooth, deep breath and then another and another, and then she takes stock of her situation.

She's lying in the trunk of a car, going God-knows-where, on a straight, fast road that can only be a freeway. She isn't angry, but only confused. She can't comprehend why this should be happening to her. She begins to hope. It was all a mistake; the men will take her home; they will let her go; they will forget about her, entirely.

She listens to the sound of tires hissing over wet concrete, and the hum of the car's exhaust. One of the men laughs and the sound of it is like a red light flashing behind the woman's eyes. The truth is bared, in that laugh. Stark and mean. There's no escape, no way to reason with these men. Her hope vanishes and, casting about, she finds a kernel of resolve she didn't know she had--a resolve that's different than the long-suffering drive of the runner. Something older and much darker. She gropes in the darkness and her fingers close around a steel bar. A tire iron.

The small determination flares in her chest and then grows stronger. She lets the physical world she is in flood into her consciousness. The pain. The rough steel beneath her back. The smells of blood and mildew and gasoline. She senses these things and the bleakness of her situation. She moves her arms and legs slowly to wring the stiffness from them. She doesn't hope, nor does she give up hope. Everything is different, because running is no longer her goal. This isn't a sporting event, and she can't afford to play by rules. Things begin to appear simple, elemental, to her and she knows without question that she is changing into something else, entirely. When the men open the trunk, she will fight and win, or fight and die. Words have become useless. Violence has brought her to this place, and now violence is the only thing that can save her.

The car slows. Her heart beats faster. She's nearly prepared, but before she goes completely over the edge she pauses, resisting the madness. Deprived of the sight of the water and the trees and the wildlife, she longs for her life to be the way it once was. Images of the people she loves come to her with photographic clarity: her mother's crooked teeth, her father's swollen belly, the floppy ears of the gentle boy she dated in high school. And then the ancient imperative rises in her and she's mortally angry at the men who stole her away, and at her old blind ways, and she knows she'll do whatever it takes to run beneath the trees with her hard, new eyes.

§ § §

Terry DeHart was raised in Portland, Oregon and is a former U.S. Marine. He now lives in the San Francisco Bay Area with his wife and three daughters, and works as a technical writer at NASA/Ames Research Center.

Terry's stories have been published in bananafish, Vestal Review, In Posse Review, The Paumanok Review, Barcelona Review, Zoetrope All-Story Extra and the first edition of Literary Potpourri.

Terry has completed an outline of his first novel, and is now "putting in the words and commas, and shit."

OCTOBER, 2002

SHORT STORIES

THE FALLS

by Beverly Carol Lucey

The window in the top left corner of the peeling gray house frames a cross-eyed Rebekkah. She's watching the road from between two bedspread curtains. The houses on this street sag all defeated like. Not worth painting. Bekka nibbles the green glitter polish off her right thumb. She wants a tattoo, but doesn't know where people get them.

Lately she's snuck out some nights, when everyone thinks she's up there just drawing weird animals in her room, like usual. She's met a few boys. The ones who hang out near Tubb's don't care one way or the other when she shows up. Long as she keeps her mouth shut. Long as she looks impressed when they talk about the things they've done, and the dumb things they are planning. She could live or die. Show up or not. But last week a new face asked her name. First one who ever did.

Now, Guy has just coasted next to the hedge with his Chevy idling, right at nine, like they said. She's leaving for good. Tonight is the night. No one notices her sliding out the back door with the frayed gym bag.

Behind her in the house, there is yelling and whispers. In the back seat of the car outside are two sleeping bags, a puffy eyed cat, and a cooler. He looked to have all the stuff they needed. Just like he said. Rebekkah is going to smoke a cigarette, turn the radio dial any time she wants to, stretch and yawn real loud. She's going to feed Jasper, and pet his fur, if Guy lets him out of the screen box. She's going to let her hand rest on Guy's leg, and who knows what after that.

Once in the car she realizes he isn't talking very much. Rebekkah keeps shooting sharp looks over at the boy's bony chin. His hands hold the wheel exactly parallel and his shoulders meld into the back of the worn, woven green bench seat. He has looked at her only once since she's gotten in. Trying to get his eye, Bek rolls down the window, then spins the knob about five times and takes a deep, deep breath. She sticks her head out of the car frame and yells like a rodeo guy. No one would let her go to the traveling fair last year, so she hid behind some bushes and heard this cowboy yelling, "Whooh yaw!"

From another leafy clump she'd watched her step brothers glue each other up with their gummed up cones of pink and green cotton candy. She'd spied her dad and his hussy wife Missy walking and stopping at every booth, laughing and bumping hips. If she'd gotten caught she'd have been dead. Step-mothers ruined everything.

But now, tonight, she finally yells out the whoops and joy she's only overheard, the ones always seemed to be coming from the next house over, or out on the street past the hedge or in the smart kids' classes in the rooms across and down the hall at school.

None of that matters now. She is out and she is never going back.

When Bek was four, her mother had died having another baby. Pa told her that Ma got sicker at the hospital. Rebekkah was pretty sure her ma just must have got sick of her, else why would she go bother having another one. Then Missy came with two sticky boys of her own. Plus, not one kid in school ever said anything sweet. They'd fired the one nice teacher. In these twelve years since, she'd mostly been told to go to her room and think about her place in the family and whether she deserved to stay.

"Take that you stupid Gai-ther-ton! I hate you all! You rotten...you..." Then she laughs and looks back in to see if Guy is smiling at her but he isn't. She reaches back into the cooler and chooses an orange Nehi to start. She'd traded a camping knife with Bobby Wallace last Saturday after he caught her looking in his back yard. Said he'd give her the knife if she let him unzip her sweatshirt and see what she got under. He'd squeezed at her a few times but now she didn't care. She just pops the cap off that bottle as pure as you please with one of the swell knife attachments.

"Where are we goin', Guy? You said a pretty place. Is it far?" But Guy has to slam on the brakes just then to avoid a deer that was all of a sudden in front of them, and he never answers. Rebekkah sees the lights go out at a one-pump store, then an old man comes out. The old man looks over at the screeching sound, then keeps moving to the side stairway and goes up some rickety steps to a half-lit couple of rooms. No streetlights are on and wet fog lazes on the headlights while the buck claps off into the woods.

When they get about fifty miles out of town, over in Franklin County, Guy pulls over to a rest stop and leads her giggling into the woods. The sound of rushing water gets really loud and a fuzzy half moon appears on top of a pointed fir. He is dragging her now, pulling on her to hurry.

"What about the cooler, Guy? What about the sleeping bags, Guy? Are we leaving Jasper alone? How are we gonna sleep without the bags, Guy? Guy? You know where you're goin? You got a house out here? Didn't you say we was goin' to find ourselves a place to live? Guy? I got a pain in my side from running so hard. I can't go no more for now. Don't be mad."

103

They are just at the edge of a ravine. The water falls so strongly that it shoots up spray to kiss the night mist. Rebekkah has never seen such natural beauty before. Her old mill town is a gritty place in summer, wears dirty slush in winter and in all the twelve years since Missy had come to fill the house, Rebekkah had never seen anything pretty except in a magazine.

Guy is breathing hard. He is looking right at her like the way he looked when he'd hatched the runaway plan. "I know where to go," he said last week. "I done this twice before." Part of his face always hangs still from Bell's palsy but the other half is finally smiling at her in the moonshine as one arm snakes around her waist and he faces her to the falls. "Just step out a little." He is nudging her, hiss panting. "You'll see something."

He promised her the most beautiful place in the world and now, at least for one wet suspended minute, she finally sees it.

§ § §

Beverly Carol Lucey has published short fiction in Portland Maine Magazine, Flint River Review 1999 (GA), Moxie Winter edition 2000 (CA) Four stories are anthologized in We Teach Them All (Stenhouse Press, Maine). Another is in the Quality Women's Fiction, 2001 (UK). Four non-fiction pieces will appear in upcoming editions of the inspirational Chocolate for Women series.

Extensive presence online include ezines: Zoetrope All Story Extra, Vestal Review, CollectedStories.com, and Millennium Shift.

The author, a life long educator, lives in Georgia, and is a member of the Georgia Writers Association.

ANCIENT HISTORY

by Jeffrey Hartman

Their father is coming. They hear his careless footsteps outside the house, scuffing up dust. Matthew thrusts the small atlas at Callie. He has been tracing with his finger the pencil line drawn from England across the south of Europe, along the craggy countries that with Africa make a mouth of the Mediterranean. Callie turns from him so swiftly her braid bats against his cheek. She gathers the items spread between them on the floor, stuffing them into a clear plastic bag. Three blue ribbons from the Carter Elementary School spring field day. A silver ring with a dark stone. A tube of lipstick long since hollowed. A photograph of their mother, torn in two.

Matthew hears the front door open. His mouth dries. He snakes himself into Callie's lap, pressing the atlas against her flat chest until its gold-edged pages splay on the underside of her chin. She pushes at him and he clings and he fears she will pinch him, hard, but instead she slides the atlas down and into the bag and the bag across the floor and under the bed just as their father enters the room.

"So, you're awake," he says in his deep voice. "Guess what? I have good news for you." He reaches down to poke a finger gently against Matthew's ribs. Matthew laughs without wanting to, writhing, until Callie hauls him from their father's reach.

"What is it?" she asks. "Are we going home? Are we going back?"

Their father scowls, pulling at his beard, and tells her to make the bed.

***

They walk to the market in the morning, watching the distant sea flash in the gaps between the buildings. Their father has business. He has decided they will stay here, in the two rented rooms of the small whitewashed house, with the narrow windows that admit light in sheaths. He has only to make one or two things happen, simple things, and they can stay as long as they like.

"Won't that be great?" he asks, and they glance at each other before nodding slowly. At the market their father has men to meet with. He leaves Matthew and Callie in the square with a group of sleek, dark-haired children. They do not speak the same language but nonetheless a game of jacks commences in the dust beside the fruit stalls, governed by gesture and tone. Callie bounces the ball high and easily swipes all of the jacks, then hands them out one by one to the other children, like a mother passing sweets. When Matthew's turn comes he cannot scoop the jacks and soon the other children do not pass him the ball. Callie takes his thin shoulders and steers him to a tree's nearby shade. She has thieved two apricots from the fruit man. Matthew lays with his head on her leg and she presses the fruit against his lips, laughing, while the juice runs under his cheekbones and into his ears.

"It tickles you," she says. "Say it tickles!"

"It tickles," he murmurs.

She laughs and spins over to hug him. She wraps her arms beneath and around his chest so tightly that he has to skip three breaths.

***

Their father explains his new opportunity. On the far side of the market square is a field. Not an ordinary field, he says. A treasure chest disguised as a field. Men have come from America to dig in the field, to unearth its treasure. He will help them, their father says. He will find them workers, a cook, a place to stay. He will speak with the landowner. Without his help, the treasures will never be found.

"Where in America?" Callie asks.

"Hmmm?"

"Where did the men come from, in America?"

Their father yawns in his chair. Matthew sees the fillings in his teeth, like spots of ink. Callie sits cross-legged on the floor, perfectly still.

"Where in America?"

"Oh, Callie, I don't know. Maybe it is Canada where they come from. Or England. Not America. I only meant that they speak English."

She opens her mouth to ask another question but their father takes his book to the terrace outside. Callie stares at him through the window and abruptly reaches under the bed to pull the atlas from the plastic bag.

"Matthew, come here."

Matthew hesitates.

"Come on already!"

They sit with their backs to the wall, beneath the window. Callie flips through the pages of the atlas, pausing here and there to set his finger on a section of map, whispering. Everything she tells him she has told him many times before.

"This was first. Listen to me. You need to remember this. It was England. There was a woman there you liked. Mrs. Jarmon. You let her brush your hair. Like mom." Matthew remembers a woman smelling like mint, with a voice that made him want to sleep. "And this was next. Down here in France. I heard him on the telephone. He thought mom had found where we were. You don't remember that, but try to remember that I told you about it. In case."

Matthew traces his finger along the jagged coastline. His sister's hands are very tan. Her nails are like pieces of shell.

"And then we had to get on the train and go over here. See how this is like a shoe? It's Italy. That's where we had to go next, because he knew someone who could help when you got sick."

He remembers the awful feeling in his chest and makes himself small beside her. "You were really sick, Matthew. I never saw someone so sick."

He insists his arm under hers. He wants to hug her. No, he wants her to hug him. Absentmindedly she drapes her arm around his neck and flips the pages. Their gold edges dazzle in the light from the window overhead. She stops flipping and he points to the page. "That's where we are now. Tunisia. Say it. Tunisia."

"Too-neez-see-uh," he says softly.

"I never heard of this place before. It's really foreign. Not even like the other places. This place is nowhere. That's why he wants to stay."

Matthew looks down at the great toothy mouth of the Mediterranean. He knows they crossed that mouth in a boat, sitting on either side of their father, accepting bits of cheese and apple that he cut for them with a folding knife pulled from his pocket. He knows he spit olive pits into his father's cupped hand. He knows that Callie vomited over the railing in the middle of the night, and afterward refused to let their father wipe her face.

***

Their father fashions them wide-brimmed hats of palm fronds, which they wear to the excavation site each day. They sit beside the pits, watching the local men from the market haul dirt and sift it through large wooden squares bottomed with wire mesh. Twice each morning and afternoon, at their father's instruction, they walk to the market to fill a bucket with water, which they then carry from pit to pit, a ladle clanging in it like a clapper in a bell. Each man smiles at them before drinking. In the late afternoons, while the men cover the pits with plastic sheets, they play tic-tac-toe on a grid drawn in the dust.

On the fourth day Callie calls out to one of the men, Ahmed, the fruit seller's son, and by pantomime convinces him to let her help him shake his sifting square. The dirt drizzles through the mesh, revealing rusted batteries, bits of china, bottletops. After lunch a fist-sized rock emerges as they shake the frame. Callie pockets it when Ahmed bends to remove a thorn from his sandal. She brings it to Matthew. Together they brush the dirt from the rock and gradually it assumes the shape of a butterfly. An hourglass. "Do you know what it is?" she asks him.

He shakes his head.

110

"It's an ax head," says a voice behind them. They turn. One of the archaeologists is leaning over them. His black eyebrows are threaded with gray. He lifts the stone. "Pretty remarkable, I'd say. Come on. Show me which pit this came from."

Callie leads him by the hand to a pit where Ahmed toils with a small pick-ax. The archaeologist lowers himself into the pit and directs the young man backward. He kneels down and removes a small broom from a hook on his belt, which he uses to whisk the dirt at his feet. With great care he uses the pick-axe to dislodge several hardened clots of dirt, then sweeps again. As Matthew watches a spot of astonishing blue appears near the archaeologist's boot.

"What is that?" asks Callie.

The archaeologist reaches for her, helps her down into the pit, hands her the little broom. She sweeps the dirt. A long edge of blue emerges. Callie begins to laugh. The blue is set in tiles, straight in some places, curved elsewhere. She sweeps along the edge until it corners, then lays her hand flat on the tiles. She stands up, raises her arms, laughing. Matthew realizes his sister is standing on something ancient, hidden, beautiful.

"What is it?" she asks again. "Is it old? Who made it?"

The archaeologist removes his glasses and wipes his brow.

"I'd say it a mosaic of some sort. Likely Roman. Very large. Excellent color. Well preserved. Stunning, really."

"But what is it?" Callie asks.

The archaeologist looks at her, tilting his head one way, then the other. He guides her to the side of the pit, off of the blue tiles, and lifts her up into Ahmed's waiting arms. "You mean, what is its picture? What does it show? Well, we won't know that until we uncover it entirely. But I think that this part we can see is one of two things. Can you guess?"

"It will be the sky," Callie predicts.

"The sky," Matthew repeats.

"Or it will be the ocean."

"The ocean," Matthew says.

"Yes, I think so, too. The sky or the sea. Equally lovely. You have brought us terrific luck. Let us do some work around it now, and tomorrow you can help uncover it. Okay?" Callie grins. She removes her palm-frond hat and throws it high into the hot wind. She takes Matthew's hand and pulls him across the field, singing a song he recognizes but cannot name.

***

The plastic bag lies between them. Their dirt-stained knees touch. The sound of rushing water comes from the outdoor shower where their father is washing. Callie joins the torn halves of the photograph and Matthew sees his mother. She stands on a driveway beside a bright red car, waving.

"Tomorrow we're going to uncover the mosaic," says Callie. "That man said so. People who lived here a long time ago made it and now we found it."

Matthew nods as he moves the halves of the photograph around, slipping them up and down so that his mother's body zips and unzips. Callie makes a fan of the atlas, flipping its pages beside her face. She slips the silver ring with the dark stone on her finger, admires it for a moment, and leans against the wall. Matthew lays his head on her leg. Somewhere outside music begins and a wailing voice flows into it. There is the sound of the running water. Matthew counts the fine blond hairs on his sister's calf, forgets the count, feels the light pouring through the window against the back of his neck, struggles to stay awake and then falls asleep.

***

Matthew is shaking. He opens one eye. His father looms above, shirtless and wet-haired, shaking Callie by the shoulders.

"I'm taking these things," their father says. "Do you hear me?"

Callie cradles Matthew's head until her father lets go.

"These don't do us any good," their father says. He holds up the empty tube of lipstick and waves it in Callie's face. "These are behind us. Do you understand? It doesn't do us any good to hold on to these. These are ancient history. I've told you guys a hundred times. The only way we can stay together is if we forget about everywhere we've been. Forget about it. Don't talk about it. Don't think about it. That's the only way."

"Why?" asks Callie quietly. "What did we do?"

Matthew tries to rise, to put himself between them, but Callie holds his head steady in her lap, smoothing his hair. Their father has the plastic bag, the atlas. He stands over them. "Tell me you understand what I'm saying."

Their father kicks her bent knee with his foot, flecking her lap with drops of water.

"Tell me."

Callie's face hovers over Matthew. He thinks of who she was before. Three years older than him, in the fifth grade. Teachers who taught her later taught him. Your sister is so beautiful, they said. So alive. He would roll his eyes and pretend to be sick.

"I understand what you are saying."

Their father turns to go, then turns back.

"What's that on your finger?" he asks, bending down. Callie makes a despairing sound only Matthew can hear and closes her hand in a fist. Their father grips her wrist and begins to pull her to her feet. He straightens her fingers one by one. Matthew slides forward, imagines himself a cannonball, a torpedo, and drives his head upward, striking his father between the legs. His father makes a small sound and collapses on top of them. As he falls his elbow strikes against Matthew's face like a club.

***

Matthew wakes in the night and touches his face, around the eyes, across the forehead. He recognizes the feel of swelling. It is worst on his left cheek. His neck is sore. He reaches across the bed for Callie, to know she is there. The sheets are in a circle around a warm spot of mattress, but she is gone. Blind in the dark he pats the length of the mattress, waiting to feel her. She is gone. He pulls the sheet high over his head and beneath its canopy he holds a finger in his mouth to keep from crying.

He falls asleep and wakes again. Callie stirs beside him, warm, her arm flung across his chest. Their father

114

stands beside the bed with a green canvas bag on his shoulder. The windows are stripes of dim light.

"Callie, Matty, come on now," he says.

Matthew kicks at the sheets and crabcrawls backward toward the corner. Callie flattens herself against the wall to give him room.

"It's okay," their father says, "really, it's okay. I'm sorry. I know it hurts, Matty. Come on now. We need to go for a walk."

They do not move. Their father reaches into his pocket and pulls out the silver ring. He offers it to Callie.

"Here. I'm going to get rid of the rest of those things but this was your mother's. You can keep it. I'm sorry for before."

Callie clambers around Matthew and reaches for the ring. She holds it in two hands, like a small animal she fears is close to death. Their father takes Matthew's arm and gently tugs him from the covers.

***

They pass through the market, its stalls empty and battened, and take the road toward the harbor. Their father strides before them without looking back, as if he cannot imagine they would not follow. They know they are leaving this dusty place, leaving with Matthew's swollen face cloaked by the empty early hour, leaving before any inquiries are made. Gulls wheel silently overhead, shadowed checks against the blueblack sky. Callie reaches for Matthew's hand. As they walk she pulls him to herself and halfsteps until their strides match. A crescent of dirt curves where her neck meets her body and a line of dried blood creases across two of

115

her knuckles. She leans close, sets her mouth beside his ear.

"Look," she says, pointing back the way they have come, back to the square where they played jacks with the other children, ignorant of their language, and ate stolen fruit during the heat of the noon hour.

"Look," she says again, nudging his head with her chin so that his eyes turn toward the field they are passing, the field where they scratched at the earth with the archaeologists. He sees his father look, too, briefly, a jerk of the neck, a hand to the brow in reflex to shield against the unrisen sun. The plastic covering the pits flaps in the wind. Matthew squints and sees the sifting frames stacked high, the mounds of dirt, the tools lined along the fencepost.

Callie removes the silver ring from her finger. She holds it up for Matthew to see and then throws it toward the field. He lunges to stop her but she is very quick and he is so slow. He hangs on her upper arm and weights her even as the force of her throw swings him around and into her legs. They collide and fall. Sitting close, Callie takes something from her pocket and unfolds his hand. Their father turns to them now, smiles thinly, beckons for them to get up and hurry. She rises to one knee and nods toward him. When he turns back away she presses into Matthew's palm a rough-edged square of stone, white and chalky on the bottom, blue on top, chipped on the sides. A square from the mosaic, a piece of the picture he knows they will never uncover, a piece of sky or sea. She leans close once more and he shivers into her warmth and when she whispers he struggles to hold his voice before repeating loudly each word she says.

"We were here. We were here. We were here."

§ § §

Jeffrey Hartman lives in Boulder, Colorado with his wife, Alice and son Will. "Ancient History" is his first published story

THE LIGHT OF SELF-RENEWAL

by Paul A. Toth

I watch from the hotel balcony, disguised by two plastic trees and a grand piano, not to mention sunglasses, a false mustache and temporary hair dye. "It's something in that voice that reassures me," says the woman, and the stranger nods. They've come to this Holiday Inn for one reason: They want me to teach them how to lie to themselves. That's why they all come, me flickering on the television, telling them in my infomercial chant, "Oh yes, you will. Yes, you can!" And yes, yes, these two will have sex tonight. Sex and magic go together, don't you know?

More people gather in the lobby, the crowd swelling by the minute, exhausted and excited. On the jet planes here they dreamt of sundecks and sailboats, European vacations and second bathrooms and people greeting them with voices full of respect and wonder. They want to be interviewed on Good Morning America and envied by the Australian guy from Lifestyles of the Rich and Famous. Some deep part of them believes in voodoo, curses, astrology, witch doctors. They trust that fate guided their remote controls to my program and hope proximity to the messenger will cast magical benefit. In another time and place, they would follow snake charmers and head dunkers.

Tom, my cameraman, drags his equipment into the lobby. He glances at me, aware something is different this time, since I've never stayed in the same hotel as the attendees. The lobby fills as Tom shoots the first few minutes of footage.

Once again, I repeat my supposed autobiography to the camera, the years delivering phone books, the studio apartment where I washed the laundry in the kitchen sink and ate frozen dinners with a Swiss army knife. Occasionally I add even more ridiculous flourishes, but no one ever challenges my veracity. Tom often warns I go too far. If only he knew about my anonymous calls to 60 Minutes, begging them to investigate the "son of a bitch who ruined my life."

Leaving him with his camera, I enter the elevator and join a group of low-level executives and would-be entrepreneurs. I stand in back, cowering inside my discomfort. For a moment, I catch an attractive blonde staring at me, squinting. Does she see through my disguise? I pretend to pick my nose and hurry off the elevator as soon as the door opens.

When I enter my room I bend over in nausea, confusion. I remove the disguise. If that woman on the elevator had seen through my disguise -- all the way through -- she would have said, "You inherited your father's estate and this is what you made of it. You failed in real business and wandered into the life of a carnival barker. You found you had a talent for it. You sell magic and we buy it, but deep down we know it's bullshit." Then she'd kiss my cheek and say, "We want the magic, stupid. We don't care if it's real or not. There's nothing to forgive."

But like a televangelist, I want their forgiveness. I imagine that woman's breath in my ear, whispering Hail Mary's like sweet nothings.

I squeeze my head, thinking of Tom. Fortunately for him, no matter what happens to me, there's plenty of work in cucumber dicers and women's mustache removers.

***

When I open my door the next morning, a blast of

119

scotch greets my nose.

"What the hell have you been doing?" Tom says. "I knocked on your door all night."

"What about you? Another shaky camera day, I take it?"

"I met a Hawaiian woman."

"Let me guess."

"Okay, she's married. You'd better get in the shower."

After I dress, Tom grabs my arm and says, "Something's going on with you, isn't it?"

"Maybe. You can sell your footage no matter what happens. Keep your camera on the audience."

"I knew it." He squeezes harder. "Carla and I are talking divorce."

There's something almost noble in Tom's ability to deny his adulterous activities bear any relation to his marital discord.

"Your plans don't rely on me, I hope?" I ask.

"You've been flirting with trouble for months. I've seen it in your eyes. Why now?"

"I've got a conscience somewhere deep inside."

"Yeah, right," he says. "Don't make me laugh."

***

Hoots and applause echo through the hotel corridors.

120

When we enter the conference room, the crowd cheers as Tom hoists the camera. I feel sadness and hatred for each and every one of them.

Tom says, "Why don't you tell them what they want to hear before they lynch us?"

I approach the podium. The crowd hushes. Air conditioners hum. Scanning faces, I cannot delineate individual faces.

"Yes, we can," someone shouts, and the crowd laughs nervously. "We really can!"

Now I see their terribly singular faces.

"No, you can't," I reply. "Let me say it again: No, you can't. You are exactly what you were yesterday. It's hopeless. It was all a lie, every word. I made a lot of money. I'm an entertainer."

Some wander away like extras on a set.

"If you prefer, I'm a magician who, through self-delusion and denial, believes his own illusions. By helping you believe your lives would change one day -- a day that would never come, of course -- I gave you the optimism of a village idiot. I can no longer offer that hope."

"I understand," a woman mumbles. I instantly match the voice to the face of the woman who stared at me in the elevator.

"Worst of all," I continue, "I've never lived in a tiny apartment. I've never eaten using a Swiss army knife. I've never once truly suffered need or want. Therefore, I will instruct my attorneys and accountants to arrange refunds."

"What will you do?" the woman asks.

"I'm going home."

I leave the microphone on the podium. It whistles as someone touches my back.

"I have to thank you," the elevator woman says. "It must be a sign, what you've done today, a sign that the good, clean, decent things I learned as a child were true all along. I really hope God doesn't punish you any more than He already has. Anyway, I forgive you. I believe in self-renewal."

I walk away, past the bar, through the hotel doors and down the street, passing signs left and right; blinking, spinning, neon signs; subtle and blunt signs; welcoming, encouraging, enticing signs; disapproving, scolding, warning signs; signs that beg and signs that beckon.

Then, somehow, my mind zooms out and I see myself walking down the street from a great distance. I look at the sun and imagine it whistling a nice little tune, something optimistic, the song of salesmen knocking on doors. Tom catches me and I feel so cheerful I pat him on the back.

"Cassette tapes."

"What?" he asks.

"A new set of cassette tapes. We'll call it, 'How to Forgive Yourself for Anything, No Matter Who You Are or What You've Done.' Does a volcano say it's sorry? That's good. Write that down. Boy, that goddamn sun can whistle. Do earthquakes visit priests and shrinks? I'm on a roll. Keep a list. The sun whistles, my friend. The sky is blue and we have things to sell."

Tom tugs my sleeve -- at least I think it's Tom until I turn and see the elevator woman.

"Horrible," she says, pointing at me. "You."

I reach out and touch her cheek. "Are you crying?" I ask, and then I laugh and laugh and laugh as words of forgiveness flood my system with the light of self-renewal.

That's a good one. I better write that down.

§ § §

Paul A. Toth lives in Michigan. His novel Fizz has just been completed and a short film based on the first chapter is in production now.

His story "Crime Writers" has been nominated for The Best American Mystery Stories by The American Journal of Print. Other credits include The Barcelona Review and Small Spiral Notebook.

FLASH FICTION

HE'LL BE THERE FOREVER

by Douglas Campbell

As the bus pulled in Kyle spotted Lena standing alone in front of the station door, the only person willing to wait out in the cold. She smiled and waved, shapeless and comical in her big puffy coat, a stocking cap gripping her head. But he hadn't forgotten the splendor beneath all that bundling: the perfect smooth curves of hips and ass, the soft, smothering warmth of her full breasts.

In half an hour, he thought, we'll be in bed together.

Lena swept into his arms as soon as his feet hit the pavement, and he had to waltz her aside so the passengers coming behind him could get off the bus. In her embrace he nuzzled up under her stocking cap to inhale her flowery hair again and kiss her little ear.

"I never dreamed six weeks could drag like that," she said.

"God almighty," he said, "it was an eternity."

"I want you," she whispered. "Let's go."

He grabbed his backpack and they headed down Bridge Street toward her apartment, holding hands. A polar wind gusted into their faces, pouring through his sweatshirt.

"Christ, I'm not dressed for this," he said. "It was forty degrees warmer in Georgia!"

Lena stopped and pulled him around to face her, then took his head in her mittened hands and kissed him, her tongue smooth, probing, and warm. "You're going to be plenty hot in a few minutes," she said. "That's a promise."

"My god, you're gorgeous," he said. "Come on, let's move!"

They set off again, practically running, but when they reached Riverside Avenue, half a block from her apartment, Lena stopped suddenly and pointed down the street.

"Oh no, there's that poor guy again," she said.

"What guy?"

"That 'Will Work For Food' guy."

Far down the street Kyle saw a tall, thin man holding a sign above his head toward the oncoming traffic and stamping his legs against the cold.

"We've got to do something for him, Kyle."

Kyle hugged himself and started stamping his own legs. "Now? You're kidding, right?"

"No, I'm not kidding. He's been out there for the past week. It's pitiful."

"But what are you going to hire him to do? Your landlord takes care of everything."

"I'm not going to hire him." She spun and faced Kyle. "Do you have any cash?"

"Thirty bucks or so."

"Let's go give it to him."

"You want me to walk way the hell down there, freezing my ass off, to hand all my cash to a total stranger? When I could be in bed with you? Does the word 'promise' ring a bell?"

"But look at him -- he doesn't have anything on but a thin jacket."

"Neither do I!"

"Oh god, I'm sorry." Lena stepped close to Kyle and drew him into her arms. "Sweetheart, you're shivering."

"From head to toe," Kyle said. "I need to get inside."

"Inside me?" Lena said.

"That would be lovely."

She kissed him again, and this time they drew it out, lingering in the rapture, the cold air around them seeming to amplify the focused heat of lips and tongues.

"God, I can almost feel you inside me already," Lena whispered when she pulled away. "Let's go."

They crossed Riverside Avenue, jogging now as they covered the homestretch.

"I don't know what I was thinking," Lena said. "It's just that I've been driving past that guy every evening after work, and I feel so guilty."

"If he's been there a week, he'll be there tomorrow," Kyle said. "He'll be there forever. Or someone just like him. We'll come out tomorrow and give him the thirty bucks."

Lena glanced at him with a mock pout. "I'm not sure I like that idea."

"You just told me how guilty you feel."

"I know -- but I kind of had a special plan for the weekend."

By that time they'd reached the steps that led up to Lena's apartment, both of them red-cheeked and winded from running and talking.

"So tell me the plan," Kyle managed to say, catching his breath.

"I've got six bottles of good wine," Lena said, "and six movies rented. I've got coffee cakes and Starbucks for breakfast, and I figure we can order out for Chinese and pizza. In other words, I thought we'd spend the weekend more or less in bed."

"Wow," Kyle said. "Could you please help me up these steps? My head's spinning."

Lena laughed and ran up the stairs, tugging Kyle along with her. "I was hoping you might have the same plan," she said as she unlocked her door and swung it open for him.

Kyle smiled and touched the tip of her nose as he went in.

"I do now," he said.

§ § §

After many years of wandering and dreaming, Doug has actually managed to hold down a full-time job for the last 13 years with the West Virginia University Libraries in Morgantown, WV.

He lives in 75-year-old bungalow that has taught him many lessons about patience and forbearance. Besides writing, Doug enjoys attempting to play Bach, or a reasonable facsimile thereof, on the guitar.

BLACK PAPER

by Kenji Siratori

my soul an embryo activates the eccentricity sky dance
of the fractal reverse side--chromosome in the moon
that is splitting in the amoeba state the word that the
brain of the desert picks and is that the death induces
the nanocrisis of the vital body that be proliferating and
emit the placenta of the horizon of the cyber=mammal
and to the remainder of the sun that drops 1 milligram
of parasite=drug of outer space to the hell of the cell
target=basement! to DNA of the vector of BABEL that
was gathered from the cerebral cortex of the clone the
DIGITAL_fly beats the guerrilla of f/0 of the micro
cosmos....cell of the cadaver bio=less_melody of the
sun interior of the womb to the negative=reproduction
gland of the material interference LOAD to the thinking
organ of etc of an embryo the last pupil of ADAM that
the spatial feeler conducts perfect=cell division in the
street on the other side of the sun is eroded to the
mirror face of chaos) (the brain of an embryo from that
sec of the clone commits suicide to the body fluid of
the blue mechanism of the sky that the mode of the
madman that escaped from my body fabricates the
skull of the absence that should fear of the sun and
loop the prosthesis of the immortality of the earth area
to the numerous pipe line in the sun and future tense of
the clone my brain the drug=organ in the over there of
the zero of the womb terrorism to the quark gimmick of
the cadaver city that quiesces or sing the fractal=love of
a cadaver in the style of the system of the direct
emotional particle that walks the crime net of the zero
gravity=embryo the madmen of my desert who earth
stimulates the digital-synapse that drifts to the
sympathy of the chaosmic chromosome to the anti-
faustic cervical vertebra of the sun be while exploding
the hallucination of the suspension of an embryo to the

cell tide in the future that clone is parasitic on the abnormal living body of the love that floats.

§ § §

Kenji Siratori is a young Japanese artist who classes himself as a 'hypermodern writer working in a digital environment.' Born in 1975, he currently lives in Sapporo, Japan. His new, exciting novel,Blood Electric is available in our book store

CHOKE

by T.K. Mancia

Alimar Mohammad Omar Mohammad Amid, or Al, as he
was known to family and friends, lay on the bed of his
Motel 6 room, bathed in the soft glow of the TV, a half-
eaten bucket of Kentucky Fried on the night table
beside him. Idly his fingers pinched a small roll of fat
around his middle. He worried that he might be out of
condition. Three years of waiting, living the 'American
Dream' had taken it's toll on his once firm, lithe body, a
legacy from his days in the training camp, from the
intense preparation of readying himself for the event
for which he was born.

He was watching a re-run of 'Roseanne'-- good figure,
lots of places to hold onto, but what a mouth! He was
thinking how the woman needed a damn good
whipping and fancying he was just the man for the job
when the phone rang shrilly. With a muttered oath and
a big bite of the Colonel's Best between his teeth, he
reached across the bed for the receiver.

'Yeah,' he grunted through a mouthful of chicken.

'Alimar Mohammad Omar Mohammad Amid?'

Al stiffened, this was *it*, this was, *the call*. Gulping down
the half masticated food, he felt a piece lodge in his
throat.

"Alimar Mohammad Omar Mohammad Amid?" the
guttural voice on the other end of the line repeated
impatiently.

"Yes," grunted Al, swallowing desperately, trying to
dislodge the blockage.

"Allah awaits you."

"Yes." Beads of perspiration dotted Al's lower lip and brow, he wiped a trembling hand over his face.

"You know what to do."

"Yes," whispered Al.

"Praise Allah."

"Praise Allah," Al wheezed, with the last of his breath.

Through a building wall of panic, Al heard the click as the call disconnected at the other end, then, throwing the receiver to the floor, he began clawing uselessly at his throat, which was now emitting a strange small whistle. He thrashed on the bed, knocking the bucket of chicken to the floor in his frenzy, his chest heaving convulsively.

With eyes bulging and face turning from dark red to mottled purple, he thought regretfully of the seventy virgins that would have been waiting for him. Not now. Not now that he had been prevented from his holy task by the stinking, infidel Western eleven secret herbs and spices.

He felt his eyes glaze as they rolled back in his head. His life's work had been foiled, fouled by the dirty, filthy, putrid, rotting bird of the Americas.

There was no glory in death by chicken.

§ § §

T. K. Mancia writes poetry and short stories and is currently working on a first novel.

PHOTO ESSAY

WOMANWORLD

by Nathan Combs

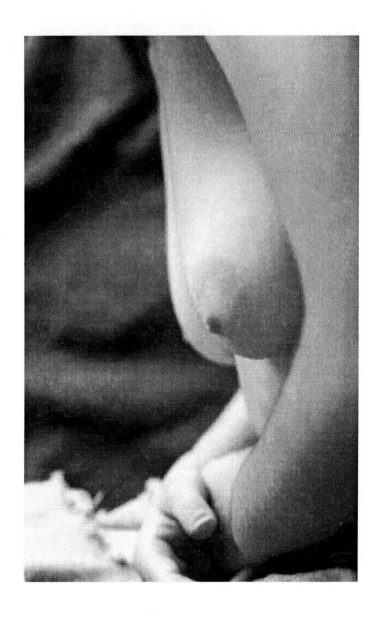

144

Nathan Combs lives in Harrisonburg, Virginia. He is 24 years old and has been shooting for ten years and having a hell of a time doing it. He'd rather work for a newspaper than anything else.

POETRY

THEORY OF EVERYTHING

by Lalo Fox

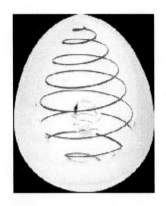

Come, string my lyre
and I will sing existence;
pluck all we have been.
and all we may become.

The lost chord found:
fundamental and harmonic,
Theme and variation,
concerto for light and time.

Not a bang - a crescendo,
all vibration at once.
The hall's walls fly away, yet
the sound still fills the room.

Wave goodbye to particulars;
duality dissolves in the roar.
The ultimate poetic justice:
Everything is tension.

Lalo Fox was born in the American Midwest at the half-century. He now lives in Appalachian Pennsylvania.

Fox has been a radio announcer, steelworker, videotape technician, engineer, night desk clerk, sandwich maker, and graphic artist, and he considers himself a 'deep historian.'

He has a poem and a micro-fiction in the premiere (June, 2002) issue of "Dreamwords".

STOP CRYING

by Giuseppe Ungaretti
Translation from the Italian by Rod Riesco

Stop killing the dead.
Stop crying, you must be silent
if you hope to hear them
instead of dying yourself.

They make that imperceptible whisper,
a sound no louder
than the growing of the grass
that's glad when no-one passes.

*Giuseppe Ungaretti (1888-1970) was born in Egypt and
spent his youth in N. Africa, being influenced by
Bedouin culture. He studied in Paris and became part of
the avant-garde movement there. Experiences in the
trenches in World War I produced his earliest mature
poems. His poetry was pared down to its essentials,*

intense and emotional. The movement known as Hermeticism was associated with him after the war. He later returned to more traditional Italian styles of poetry and taught at universities in Brazil and Rome. His selected poems have been translated into English by Allen Mandelbaum (1975).

§ § §

TANKA

by Rod Riesco

Clear frosty morning:
plum blossom whiter than white
as we kiss goodbye
one car groans up the steep track
the day fills with blue perfume

§ § §

Rod Riesco was born in 1949. He lives in Lancashire, England, and works as a freelance translator. A writer of poetry and short fiction, he is Secretary of the Bank Street Writers group in Bolton, Lancashire, and General Editor of the group's magazine, 'Current Accounts'. He also runs an on-line poetry broadsheet, The Jumping Cat.

THE MOMENT

by Eric Bosse

1.

Take off your shoes
& go to the water,

walk the river path
where buds & nubs
shirk off the cloak
of another late snowfall.
Walk to the rock pile

where last Summer's snakes
hide under layers
of skin-whispers,

shadows of Zero,
cold stones.

Take two stones
in your hands,
clack them together
& stack them again.

This is how rhythm
begins & ends.
Now listen.

Dirt under foot,
green leaves,
blue & white sky:

this moment
is a mountain.
It is all you
will ever need.

2.

It's easy to say
this moment is all
you will need,
but you'll need more
when the laundry piles
up & the dishes
& the days --

when melon rinds
draw flies into
the air of your
kitchen

& your bedroom smells
of well worn clothes.

When this moment goes,
when the others are long gone,
take off your shoes

& go to the river again.

3.

This river
flows through
the field
at the center
of the universe.

4.

Stand in the weeds
& throw a stone
to the other side,

then sit in half lotus,
head bowed low,
& listen to the water
flow like a cello
through its slow
descending scale.

Ask the river
questions
about a dog
by the side of the road,

or the woman
at the laundromat
who stared the last
time you went,

or the pull that
was not gravity
as you leaned over
the sidewalk
from fourteen storeys up,

or the way your
coffee cup
overflows
and you forget
to listen
to your breath
as you wipe the spill.

Ask the questions
that gather in piles
like laundry
during the time
you're away from
the river's edge.

5.

This moment
is not a mountain.
It is only
a river. A river.

*Eric Bosse is a writer, filmmaker and Special Education
teacher living and working in Colorado.*

*He has published stories in Exquisite Corpse. Mississippi
Review, Zoetrope-All Story Extra, Linnaean Street,
Nubrite, and others.*

*Eric has made three short films and a long one, and
continues to work on a novel and two screenplays.*

*Eric is also the editor of the new online journal,
The God Particle which will debut November 1st, 2002.*

ESSAY

OUR WAR

by Ronald F. Currie, Jr.

*We were born in or around 1975, the
year Gerald Ford declared publicly
that the war in Vietnam--the last
grand conflict by which an American
generation could define itself--was
"over."*

*

When we boys grew up, we left America for Europe and
Asia and Africa. We went as students and as tourists--
never as soldiers. We doffed our ballcaps in the
reconstructed cathedrals of France and Germany,
peered at the grainy black-and-white photos of their
ruins and tried to reconcile these with the new stained
glass and reinforced vaulted ceilings. We walked the
grounds at Dachau, snapped somber photographs, then
rode the train back into Munich and spent the night
dancing on tables and drinking beer from giant steins.
We smelled the stink of simulated trenches at the
Imperial War Museum in London, saw shadows burned
onto the ground at Nagasaki, and watched the sun sink
below the smoky skyline of what is now known as Ho
Chi Minh City.

We knew, though, that the dried brown blood of history
was insufficient, and we came home to America without
any excuse for the sorrow and alienation that had
descended on us. So we left again, most of us, and
came home again, still short of the epic violence which

would serve to excuse our malaise.

Things got worse. We all played the part of disaffected youth, which is to say we drank and drank and didn't do much else unless we were forced to. Many of us, myself included, dropped out of college.

Our fathers, who had fought in Vietnam, could not understand. After all, they were the only American generation ever to lose a war; yet they'd managed to get on with their lives. My own father still does not understand, even though, in an effort to bridge the gap between us, I subjected him to the great indignity of discussing how we felt about each other. This was in the hospital. Our conversation was set up and mediated by a case worker on the psych ward. My father and I sat facing each other in molded plastic chairs in a room which was otherwise empty. I cried. He did not.

Shame, shame!

Give me a German machine-gun nest, a Viet Cong tunnel complex, a cave teeming with angry desperate North Koreans, anything, ANYTHING but my father and I alone, in a room empty except for the chairs we sit in, with me wanting to die for no damn good reason, and without a war of my own.

Shame, shame!

*

We knew, at a very young age, that war was our fate and our inheritance. The mythology of the American fighting man, from Rickenbacker to Rambo, was in our hearts. We played our games with great seriousness, for we knew they were preparation as much as recreation. Four-square and sandlot baseball were life-or-death, and sometimes we were bloodied.

160

We absorbed patriotic rhetoric like sponges. We recited daily our Lord's Prayer and our Pledge of Allegiance. We did not know-no one could have-that we'd been born on the cusp of a long period of peace, unprecedented in American history. We did not know-no one could have-that we would pass our best fighting years at the water cooler and watering hole, in neckties and soft shoes, overfed, well-rested, fat and healthy.

Too late, we realized that we'd become, in Hitler's words, the cowardly children of Democracy.

Nothing can produce so shameful and weak a generation as a few decades of peace.

*

In the early nineteen-eighties, when we still believed we would someday be men, we had Libya as a primer. We heard the adults saying war on the telephone and at the dinner table, and we were ready. We had no way of knowing that Libya was a small and comparatively powerless country, no real threat to us. So we prepared for an invasion. We photocopied encyclopedia entries on Libya, took our Boy Scout knives and canned goods pilfered from our parents' kitchen cupboards, and headed for ravines and backyard groves all over the country. We built lean-tos and crude tiny ramparts. We dug in and waited for the Libyan invaders.

While we waited, Reagan rained steel and fire down on Tripoli. He buried Quadaffi's children alive, and that was that.

When the tuna fish and canned green beans ran out, we went home untried, our bones stiff and aching with the cold.

*

161

We had reached an age, too, when we began to appreciate the fighting legacy our fathers and grandfathers had created. How impressed we were with the framed photos of familiar-looking young men in uniform! How their medals shone! How colorful and enchanting were their ribbons and epaulets, hidden away in attics, then unearthed again by us on dull rainy Sundays!

We found pictures of dead friends, love letters from girls who'd come and gone long before our mothers and grandmothers, boot camp yearbooks, photos of London and Paris and Guam and Hong Kong and Saigon. We didn't feel guilty for snooping, because all these things were ours by rights. Our legacy. Our inheritance.

Not to be, not to be. Peace reared its head and stayed a while, and we were left to find a new path to manhood.

*

Desert Storm was a wash--too soon for most of us, who were still sophomores in high school. The Mother of All Battles turned out a lame duck, and we entered our late teens with no war, no more Evil Empire--nothing but quiet prosperity.

We never stood a chance. We see that clearly now, and it explains a lot.

*

There are nights even now, on the other side of twenty-five, when we lie awake and plead with our fathers, and our grandfathers' ghosts:
Please, we beg them. Give us our war. We need to find you, and this is the only way.

162

Give us our USS Maine, our Pearl Harbor, our Gulf of Tonkin--make us believe.

Give us our Tojo, our Mussolini, our Hitler and Ho Chi Minh--help us hate righteously.

Give us our Iwo Jima, our Omaha Beach, our Tet--let us die heroes, and mount our photos on the wall next to yours and remember us with pride.

We are cowards. We want only to be, like you, one of the Few, the Proud.

Time is running out. Already we are past the age when you killed and came home, eyes fixed, mouths forever silent. And yet we have done nothing.

With what is left of our meager will, we demand you give us our war.

It is the only thing a man ever truly owes his son.

§ § §

Ronald F. Currie, Jr. is a native of Waterville, Maine, where he still lives with his dog.

His work has appeared/is forthcoming in Glimmer Train Stories, Carve Magazine, InPosse Review, and other publications. He received the 2002 Martin Dibner Memorial Fellowship in fiction.

BOOK REVIEW & INTERVIEW

TIME FOR ALEXANDER by Jennifer Macaire

by Beverly Jackson & Shaula Evans

It was with some trepidation that I opened *"Time For Alexander"*--the first novel (in a series to come) by Jennifer Macaire. My sources said it was about Alexander the Great and time travel--and since historical fiction and sci-fi genres were not my normal taste, I was hesitant. But knowing and trusting Ms. Macaire's skills, having read much of her short fiction, I pushed forward in curiosity, and am happy that I did.

This novel is as much fun as a Mardi Gras parade. It lopes across the terrain of romance novels, historical fiction, magical realism, and science fiction--costumed, its cheek poked out by a devilish tongue, spoofing the genres, never taking itself too seriously, and yet cleverly snaring it's reader in a gloriously intriguing plot about a young woman journalist who time-travels back through history to interview Alexander The Great. What follows, after she awakes under a pomegranate tree, is a hilarious, mind-bending tale of a modern woman immersed in the ancient throes of sex, love, quite a bit of *vino*, war, death, and ever so much more.

Using historical facts for a springboard, Ms. Macaire leaps into the waters of pure imagination, and creates a unique novel, the likes of which you're not likely to find anywhere. Ashley, our journalist heroine, narrates with the certainty and casualness of a woman who knows who she is, and has all the heart and daring of her own to take on any great world conqueror. It's a downright hoot. Macaire deftly submerges Ashley in the kingdom's culture and mores with such credible logic that it makes reading the saga pure fun, with us rooting for the 'good guys' all the way.

In this literally epic writing project, Ms. Macaire deftly tackles the authorial challenges of historical research, cross-genre writing, and publishing an unconventional novel. In the following conversation by email, she discusses her craft and the adventure of publishing *Alexander* with me and LP Book Review Editor Shaula Evans.

***

Jackson: Hi Jennifer. I really enjoyed your book!

Evans: Jennifer, I wanted to let you know that I read the book start to finish in one sitting and I enjoyed it tremendously.

Macaire: I appreciate your kind words.

Jackson: How did you ever get the idea to write *Time for Alexander*? What prompted you?

Macaire: I know it sounds trite, but I'd just read a biography that left me frustrated. The professor admitted that most of what was written about Alexander was conjecture, and that no contemporary writings about him existed. I decided to write a quick sketch, just to see if I could get a bit of the essence of Alexander's story on paper. I started writing a short story about a journalist who goes back in time to interview him, and Alexander just took over. His character seemed to come to life, and when he kidnapped the journalist, I knew I was going to have to make the short story into a novel.

Jackson: When I finished this book, I knew I wasn't finished with this story. This looks like it's going to be a series of books, am I right?

Evans: I wondered the same thing. What plans do you have for future books?

Macaire: The funny thing is, I only planned on one book, but Alexander had such a strong character that I couldn't fit him into any other plot than his own life, which was incredible enough as it is and took up four books. But I couldn't let him die in Babylon, so his time-traveling wife saves him, and they go to Gaul and then to the land of the Eaters of the Dead to search for the Thief of Souls.

The story is quite interesting, and a lot is based on time, on the possibility of changing the future and the idea that fate does or does not exist. The Greeks believed in fate, while Ashley, who comes from the future, does not believe in anything. She doesn't believe in any sort of Gods, so it's always a nuisance when Apollo talks to her. She's scientific and intellectual, and she can't 'relax' and let things happen. I had a lot of fun making her interact with Alexander. They complement each other.

In all, there are seven books in the series. All done, all

final drafts. I'm waiting for the contract for the rest of them, but like anything else, it depends on the results of book one, I suppose. I can't imagine not publishing them, so I have a couple of options open right now. The best would be that they come out as soon as possible--I have several people threatening me if the other books don't appear. Soon.

Jackson: (laughs) Did you mean for this book to come out so funny and campy? You DO know it's fun and campy, right? Was this intentional?

Macaire: I wrote an introduction for the first draft where I said, "The history is solid but the book is fiction and walks that fine line between fantasy and reality." I also wrote, "I wanted this book to be fun, most of all." So of course I knew it was funny. There are some places in the book that still make me laugh aloud, and that's a good sign, considering I've read the book at least a hundred times just editing it. Campy is a good word for the sort of humor I was aiming at. Actually, while writing I wasn't aiming at anything. It just felt right to take the book in that direction. It is a character-driven book, and Alexander is so larger-than-life that if there wasn't that element of absurdity it would not have worked. Plexis is actually the character that adds all the humor to the story, and I think he's always been my favorite.

Jackson: I liked that character too. I was astonished at some of the things I learned about their everyday lives, not your mundane Encyclopedia Britannica fare! How much research was necessary to write this?

Macaire: I have read at least three complete biographies of Alexander since high school. The last one was by an Italian professor who quoted many of Aristotle's letters, Darius's letters and contested the letters that were supposedly written by Alexander. He claimed that all Alexander's writings were destroyed and that everything written about him was conjuncture. That certainly sparked my interest; it was a refreshing point of view, and it opened a vast window in the historical world that had largely been closed by writers such as Plutarch who has long been the 'last word' on Alexander. Plutarch wrote Alexander's biography four hundred years after Alexander's death. Plutarch was Greek, and the Greeks were always a bit touchy on the subject of those upstart Macedonians - Philip and Alexander. No matter they'd certainly saved Greece from becoming a fief of Persia.

Then there are the modern historians; very serious, learned people, who always seemed to want to press Alexander into a modern mold. One book that both helped me and incensed me at the same time was 'In the Footsteps of Alexander the Great' by Michael Woods. He actually trekked across Asia, following Alexander's army. That, for me, was a Godsend. It took away having to research distances, time and geography, which were necessary for making Alexander's voyage 'real'. At the same time, Mr. Woods felt the need to be politically correct, and insisted in trying to find a 'reason' for Alexander's making war on all the tribes along the way. He also tried to compare Alexander's emotions and feelings to that of a modern man. Mr. Wood's interpretation of Alexander didn't work for me, the same way that Mary Renault's books on Alexander did work--but had nothing to do with Alexander. I love her books, but I never got a feeling for Alexander as a human being, and I feel very strongly that he was human.

Evans: Is it historically correct in its details or did you take some poetic license?

Macaire: I did take poetic license, especially after Book Four, when Alexander is saved. But then again, some historians think Alexander didn't die, and that he was smuggled out of Babylon. The battles are all in context, the people around him (except for his time-traveling wife) existed, his movements (thanks to Mr. Woods) are exact, and the customs and even the toothpaste was heavily researched. I used molded glass, because blown glass didn't exist back then, nor did paper. The Greeks were finicky about cleanliness, and the Egyptians were even worse. (Body odor was considered a sin) So there will be a few preconceptions about that time period that will surprise some. I got a kick out of finding out what they brushed their teeth with. Oh, and no stitches. They cauterized everything. That must have hurt.

Jackson: Are we going to find out what happens to Ashley? I'm dying to know if she gets her child back, if she lives out her life there, if she ever makes it back to modern day to tell the tale? You got me!

Macaire: Well, don't worry! Ashley lives to tell her tale, though she never goes back to her own time. She gets the chance though--remember when she mentions that someone had already been sent to interview Alexander? Well, he lies dying on his pallet, but Ashley meets the time--traveler, and he mistakes her for Roxanne. (Which does not please her.)

Jackson: Do you think you've created a new genre? This doesn't really fit sci-fi or magical realism or mainstream novels, does it?

Macaire: It fits everywhere in a sense. It is historical, and I convinced the Historical Novel Society to review the book. (Coming out in December 2002.) Romance reviewers loved it, although one romance magazine primly pointed out, that "because it was not a monogamous relationship, it could never be classified as 'Romance'", but added, "This book is fantastic!"

Science fiction magazines have claimed it as their own, one saying "Ms. Macaire has used pure science fiction to take us on an incredible journey..." So it's nice that everyone has found something to relate to in this book. But to tell the truth--I wasn't thinking about any of that when I wrote.

I was just following the story as Alexander, Plexis and Ashley evolved. It is their story, and everything else sort of faded into the background. I never once thought about genre as I wrote, I never do unless I'm writing science fiction. In March 2003 Novel Books, Inc. Books will publish Virtual Murder, a sci-fi book. Then there is another historical, 'Angels on Crusade', based on the Crusades, and which I loved to write. I'm looking forward to that book but it doesn't have a publishing date yet.

Evans: What was your biggest literary goal with the novel?

I had several goals. I wanted to pull off the challenge I'd set myself - to write a literary novel that would be accessible to everyone and fun to read. I wanted a 'I can't put it down!' book that would make people think, that would bring up subjects that were taboo such as love between men and infidelity and make them appear so natural that they became accepted by readers--as they were accepted in that time period. But most of all, I wanted readers to experience a shift in their perception of life, and to learn from the book--whether it be about Alexander, ancient toothpaste or whatever!

Jackson: Did you have any trouble finding a publisher? Did the publishing world understand what you were up to? I notice the book is published in Australia.

Macaire: I can imagine Homer trying to sell his Iliad to a modern publisher, and it's more or less what happened with me and the agents and publishers I approached.

Homer: "Describe my book's genre? Well, it speaks of war, so it could be an adventure, but it has a love story between Hector and his wife...oh yes, and it has paranormal elements, there's Cassandra, she sees the future. There are religious factors, the gods and goddesses are always appearing and there is a definite historical slant, after all, it's about the siege of Troy, but there is quite a bit of humor. What do you think?"

Publisher: "I'm sorry, it doesn't fit our publishing needs right now. It's well written, but doesn't match any category. We wish you the best of luck with another publisher."

Homer: "I have another one too, this one is called 'The Odyssey' and I think it could be classified as a travelogue." He hesitates. "Adventure travel with elements of romance and the paranormal."

Publisher: "Send in the first three chapters and a synopsis. We'll get back to you in about a year. But don't get your hopes up. History books are not selling, series are out of the question for an unknown, cross-genre is not acceptable for traditional publishers and you haven't been published before."

I waited four years before finding a publisher. Most editors loved the story, but no one wanted to take a chance on something so radically different than what is 'out there'. I had a problem with the fact that Alexander had more than one wife, that he was bisexual, and that Ashley is not faithful to Alexander. She falls in love with Plexis, and Plexis is in love with Alexander, and the whole story sort of overwhelmed some people. One person sent back my manuscript with 'I can't handle this!' in big red letters. That was a low point, but I never got upset about it. I love this series, and to tell the absolute truth, even if it hadn't been published, I still would have been content. I truly love to read these books, and that, to me, is why I wrote them. Because they are fun to read and to entertain. Even if it's only myself.

Evans: Since some of the Literary Potpourri readership consists of writers, can you share with us some insights with us into the process behind publishing the novel?

Macaire: I wrote the series in four years - there are seven books, each about 300 pages. I thought about having it as a trilogy - but try selling a nine hundred-page book when you're just starting out! I tried traditional publishers, but as I said above, they wouldn't take the chance. Most were extremely nice - all loved the book but were afraid it wouldn't sell. Agents were the worst - I tried 30 agents before deciding to represent the book myself. I chose Jacobyte in Australia for several reasons - I figured they would be less puritan than the American publishers and they had a good, eclectic selection. I read a few of their books before submitting to them, and I was thrilled when they offered to publish *Time for Alexander.* I had an agent look over the contract and she pronounced it all right. I designed the cover and those of the next six books using the same statue of Alexander the Great. I am glad the book is finished, glad it's finally published but mostly glad that it's being read and appreciated.

Jackson: What other kind of reading do you do? Do you read light or serious fiction?

Macaire: I read anything with words on it. Since I could put 'b' and 'a' together and get 'ba', I've been reading. My favorites are Tolkien, Ray Bradbury, Dorothy Dunnett, The Discworld series, Douglas Adams, Cold Mountain, Water Touching Stone, Amy Tan, James W. Hall, Robert Ferringo, The God of Small Things, Dreams of My Russian Summers...Well, I could go on for pages.

Shakespeare will always be my all time favorite.

Evans: At what points does your own life or personality intersect with your characters?

Macaire: I don't know, really. I can say I was very involved with them as I wrote the book - I think Plexis is my favorite character, and I had the most fun developing his persona. Ashley was difficult because she was so cold and couldn't show her feelings in the beginning, so it was hard to make the reader like her. In the first few drafts she came off as too standoffish, so I had to re-think her. I had to 'get into her skin' in order to bring her to life. She and I share a few traits; we don't have any prejudices and we're both shy about showing our feelings, but otherwise we're nothing alike!

Evans: What are you most excited about with this book?

Macaire: I am elated at the reception I've gotten. Because it was turned down by so many agents and publishers, I had begun to think A: It would never get published, and B: My book was somehow flawed. Most rejections stated that the book was not right for the market, that historical fiction was not 'in' and that a book with the subjects I brought up would not sell. It is such a relief and a joy to find that readers react the way I hoped they would - So far I've gotten nothing but positive feedback.

Evans: Is there anything else you would like readers to know about the genesis of the book?

Macaire: The genesis was the easy part - I guess. Stopping was hard! I think I could have gone on and on. I'm looking forward to having the rest of the series come out. I won't give anything away, but I will say that Ashley saves Alexander in Babylon, and they travel north in search of the Thief of Souls, a real character in

176

the mythology of ancient Gaul. They also go to Rome, Carthage and the British Isles. Actually, looking back, I'm amazed. I'm also grateful for my family for putting up with me while I wrote. From my husband who didn't notice the dust or complain about the pile of laundry and my son Alex who gave me ideas, to Julia who was so good, and especially to Sebi - who would make dinner for all of us while I 'played on the computer!'

Jackson: What would you like to say to your readers and your potential new readers?

Macaire:I hope, of course, that they love my book! I realize it's not for everyone, but I do hope it entertains. I want my readers to know that I don't take myself seriously, but that I do take them seriously, and I feel an obligation to write as well as I possibly can. I think books have an obligation to entertain, to educate, to fascinate and to pose questions. I hope I've done all this, and if I have, then I'm pleased. I will admit to loving e-mail, and I will be glad to answer any questions anyone has about the books or characters.

Editor's note: Since this interview, Jacobyte has agreed to publish the rest of the Alexander series, and Book #2 is now scheduled for January 2003.

§ § §

Jennifer Macaire is an American freelance writer/illustrator. She was born in Kingston, NY and lived in Samoa, California and the Virgin Islands before moving to France. She attended Parsons school of design for fine art, and Palm Beach Junior College for English literature. She worked for five years as a model for Elite. Married to a professional polo player, she has three children.

After settling in France, she started writing full time and published short stories in such magazines as PKA's Advocate, The Bear Deluxe, Nuketown, Anotherealm, Linneaen Street, Inkspin, Mind Caviar (for the August 2002 launching) and the Vestal Review. One of her short stories was nominated for the Pushcart Prize.

She has written a series of seven fiction novels based on the life of Alexander the Great - the first, 'Time for Alexander' published by Jacobyte Books in April 2002. Her science fiction novel 'Virtual Murder' will be published by Novel Books, Inc. in March 2003. Website: Iskander

MID MONTH SURPRISE

VICIOUS CIRCLE

by Brian Coté

George opened his eyes. He saw lights shining against the far wall. They appeared and disappeared over and over again. Alarmed and confused, he sat up slowly, and quietly eased himself off his double bed.

Being careful to stay low and out of sight, he crept to the window, peered out. Under the streetlight he could see an old-model Cadillac turning slowly round and round in the circle drive in front of his house. The car must have been driving around for a long time to wake him up. The headlights strobed through the thin, patterned curtains at his bedroom window every two seconds, casting long shadows across the walls.

A single streetlight illuminated the scene. The windows in all the adjacent houses were dark. The car making its steady, slow circle was the only moving object in sight.

Dressed in light pajamas, George made his way down the stairs. Everything was quiet in the empty house. Only the faint hum of the car's engine could be heard. He passed by the kitchen and through the living room furnished with only a chair and an old television set. The headlights splashed through the darkness in the living room. When he reached the door, George paused for a moment with his hand resting on the handle. He took in a deep breath and then stepped out into the night.

Barefoot, he crossed the dewy lawn and stood on the curb with his hands in his pockets, watching the car turn round and round. The driver must not have seen him, because he didn't stop. Looking closer, George could barely discern a dark figure behind the wheel.

He grew angry. Suddenly he stepped off the curb, and when the car came around, he chased after it, banging on the hood with the flat of his hand. "Hey!" he yelled. The car drove on, and George stopped, waiting for it to come around again. When it did, he chased it and banged on the roof again. "Hey, God damn it!" he yelled indignantly. But the car drove on.

When the car came around for the third time, George stepped out into its path and laid his hands on the hood, as if bringing it to a stop himself - a tiny Hercules in the dark. The engine hummed. The hood was warm beneath his hands.

"What the hell's wrong with you, buddy?" George yelled. "You're waking everyone up, driving around like that."

He felt his anger welling in his eyes. George looked at the dim figure behind the wheel, but couldn't make him out. Then he heard the sound of the car doors unlocking. The driver leaned over the seat, and the passenger's side door swung open. An uncomfortable moment passed, as George stood with his hands still on the hood, deciding what to do.

Finally he walked over and got in.

Without saying a word, the driver put the car in gear and continued his circle.

George studied him. He wasn't old, maybe twenty-five or twenty-six, and was dressed in a rough, dirty shirt and an out of date tie, which hung loosely around his neck. His hair was unevenly trimmed and there was a day's growth of beard on his chin. He looked tired, but still his eyes were focused on the road in total concentration. In contrast to his appearance, the inside of the car was extremely neat and tidy. George rubbed his feet on the floor; there was no dirt, and when he stuck his fingers into the ashtray in the armrest, he found it spotlessly clean. Only two things were out of place: a newspaper on the seat between them and a carton of eggs that had slide across the dashboard and was pressed against the front windshield. George eyed the driver nervously.

"What's your problem, buddy?" George asked. "You can't be driving like this at--" he looked at the clock in the dashboard "--three o'clock in the morning. People are trying to sleep."

The driver didn't say anything. His attention was focused on the street.

"Did you hear me, God damn it?" George asked, becoming irritated.

"I heard you," the driver said, and gave George a hard look. "Trust me, man. If I could get out of this any other way, I'd do it. I wouldn't be here. That's for sure."

"What are you talking about?"

"I'm talking about being here and driving. If I could get outta this circle any other way, I'd do it. I wouldn't be here driving around like a maniac."

"But you *are* driving around like a maniac."

"That's 'cause I'm stuck."

George breathed out impatiently.

"Stuck?" George asked. "Stuck where? Why are you here? Why are you driving around in front of my house at three o'clock in the morning, waking people up? They have to work in the morning. It's Wednesday for Christ's sake. What the hell's your problem?"

The driver looked over at him sympathetically, as if George were a small, confused child.

"Have you ever heard of a vicious circle?"

"I think so," George said. "What is it?"

"It's a philosophical term--when you assume the truth of an argument when you state it. Like saying: 'I believe in God, because the Bible says he's real.' 'Well, how do you know the Bible's true?' 'Because God wrote it.' You haven't really said anything, and you definitely haven't proven anything. You've just given your opinion. It's circular logic. Understand?"

"I guess so."

"Well, that's where I'm at right now in life. I'm stuck. I've assumed everything; I've made a circle that I can't get out of. I mean, I just got engaged, so now I have to move away, right? I have to quit my job, I have to leave all my friends and my family. I'm stuck. Fate's sucked me in and I don't know how to get out. But, you know, sometimes I really don't care. I mean, I love her and my job sucks here anyway and a couple of my best friends've just screwed me over real good and my family'll always be around. So it's like my life's falling apart and I really don't care. I should, but I don't. I mean, sometimes I do, but not really. I worry about not worrying. I guess that's post-modern, right? Why is that?"

"I don't know."

"I don't know either, but I'm trapped, either way. I mean, I could get out of it all, if I wanted to. I could stay here or run away from her or break off the engagement.

184

I don't know. It'd be worse if I did that. So I'm stuck. No matter what I do, life's gonna get more difficult. And that's just depressing. The only option I have is to choose how difficult I want it. An' what kinda choice is that?"

"It's not."

"I know. So here I am--alone in my car, driving round and round, trapped in a circle. I made it, I guess, and that's what's important. I thought, 'If I can make my own circle, and just drive round and round, 'til it's so normal that I don't even know I'm driving anymore, then I'm free. When I can take my hands off the wheel and the car'll drive all by itself, then Fate's finally taken over."

"What?"

"I know it sounds crazy, but someday it'll happen-- maybe not tonight, maybe not tomorrow, but the day after or the day after that. Someday." He slapped the steering wheel in emphasis. "When I break out of that turnaround, I can break out of that loop of logic and do something for real. I can make a real decision, make my own decisions. I'll have finally beaten Fate."

"All by driving in a circle?"

"Breaking out's the point, but you have to drive to get there first. You know what I mean? You have to take all that nonsense and forget how stupid it is. Then, when you're finally ready to take it all seriously--I mean real seriously--you can finally see how absurd it all is. But maybe you don't have those problems, living in a house like that." The driver pointed to George's house, a modern, two-story home with a trim lawn and finely carved woodwork.

"I've got my own problems."

"Ya? Like what?"

"Who are you to ask?"

"Just a guy driving."

George sighed heavily. "Lots of problems, but I can take care of them myself."

"Ya?" the driver asked. "You're a better man than me then." He paused and looked at George. "You sure you don't want to talk about it?"

"I'm sure."

The driver focused on the road, and George lowered his head in thought. The egg carton on the dashboard made a low, squeaking noise, which broke George's concentration. He looked up at it, sitting there in front of him.

Suddenly the driver slammed on the breaks, and the carton flew into George's hands. The driver smiled at him.

"Damn," George said.

"They're real delicate," he said, and took the carton from George's hands. "Nice catch, by the way."

"Thanks."

The driver weighed the carton in his hand, opened it, and held an egg in front of his face, considering it.

"You know, they don't really use real eggs anymore. Not like they used to. I mean, ya, they still come out of chickens, but there aren't any embryos in them. They're empty. Isn't that horrible?"

"It's pretty strange."

They sat next to one another for a moment in silence.

"Well," the driver said, "I guess I'll get going. I'll catch you later."

"Ya? OK...bye."

George stepped out of the car and was ready to shut the door, when the driver said, "Hey, wait a sec."

George leaned in, to see what he wanted. The driver handed him the egg he'd been looking at.

"Have an egg, man," the driver said. "It's on me."

"Thanks."

George held the egg up in parting and returned to his lawn. The car crept steadily round and round. It's headlight splashed across all the house fronts. He watched it and weighed the egg in his hand. Then without warning he threw it at the car, where it splattered across the windshield in a sticky explosion. The car came to a stop and George ran into his house.

He slammed the door shut and leaned against it firmly, listening intensely.

The driver was laughing from the street. "You're a better man than I am," he yelled. He honked his horn three times. The blasts rang out horribly loud, destroying the delicate silence. Then the car roared off into the night, leaving the street deserted.

§ § §

Brian Coté lives in Michigan and just received his bachelor's in German. Now he lives at home with his parents, reads too much, writes a little, and is waiting for the money to roll in so he can go to Germany and work on his master's and doctorate.

This is his first published story.

NOVEMBER 2002

SHORT STORIES

OUT OF THE UNIVERSE ENDLESSLY CALLING

by Tom Sheehan

Far ahead of him Knock Craften could see the last of
the lead-pack bike riders sprinting around a slow bend
in the road. The Pan Mass Challenge 200-mile bike ride
across the state to raise funds for cancer was in full
bore. 3600 riders on the move for two days, Sturbridge
to Provincetown on the tip of Cape Cod. Then the
yellow shirt of that rider disappeared, roadside
greenery swallowing it up. Behind Knock the 27 riders
of his team spread out in a long line, their purple shirts
making them look like a hive of bees on the move, the
cluster lengthened by their arduous travel. Team Vanish
they called themselves, in hopes of eradicating the
disease. Eighty-five miles had flown under their wheels
since their early morning start in Sturbridge. Now, again
as it had all morning, the impulse was coming on
strong, from its unknown and ethereal source, but this
time it had an uninterrupted resonance. And it was
pulling at him, having an oblique reference coming out
of trees and brush on his right. It was irrefutable, that
calling, a pulling, the impulse of gods he thought.

Then he saw a break in the trees and an angled road
slamming off to the southeast, sidelined by trees,
stones of an old stonewall marker. That limitless call
was entirely for him and he knew he was going down
that road. He jerked up on the seat, jammed down on
the pedals, sprinted ahead of his team, and turned
down the side road. Almost to a man the team twisted
like a whisper into that detour and swung in behind
him. He appeared to be the captain of a ship, or the
queen bee switching hive locations.

One man of his team, though, the last in line, did not

make that turn.

That rider cursed vehemently, looking ahead to where the last yellow jersey had gone out of sight, where the road to the layover stop in Bourne waited. Spitting in the gutter, he hollered, "Cocky son of a bitch is going the wrong way. Wait'll they get him in front of the cameras, his mighty ass will be mud." Paris Gallber could almost see the whole scenario. His mouth watered at the image.

Gallber, of course, had no idea that for twenty-seven years of Knock Craften's life, music endlessly called him out of the spread of the universe, coming on him at odd times like a homing intelligence, but one without a language. Never once had he told anybody about it, not his parents, or his siblings, or his best friend, John Wellborn, who he knew was in the pack behind him. And it was only in his start into adolescence that he realized not everybody heard this song. If asked to explain he would not have said it was music, but more an awareness of something far beyond the capability of his mind to understand. Out of a void it came, possibly down the crook of centuries, or on an uncharted line from the vast unknown.

But it came directly to him.

Now here he was, on his bicycle, a $2400 beauty, leading his team in this 200-mile ride to raise funds for cancer research, with 80 or 85 miles behind them. The hills of western Massachusetts had been steep, at times the traffic heavy. The humidity was a factor for some of the older riders, and the August noon sun was a hammer beating on all of them. The frequent water stops were a gift, and though they were not in a race, he could feel the energy trying to bust loose in his frame. But, as promised, they were going to ride as a team, to finish as a team.

194

How could he possibly explain this last move of his, this offhand spurt down a strange road?

Paris Gallber was trying to do just that at the curve at the lake, stopping at a news van, pointing back over his shoulder. "I don't know what's wrong with the captain of my team, but he just took the whole damn crew down a wrong road! Can you imagine such idiocy, such lack of planning. Thinks he's the big-time honcho on this ride. I'll bet the other news hounds will be all over his case before this day is over!" Sweat poured off his face, a twist of one corner of his mouth caught pellets of that perspiration as if they were his sole sustenance of ride.

Yet down a long grade of that strange road, his wheels catching sunlight like the blades of a fan, like the magic of a spinning semaphore flashing a hidden message, Knock Craften sped. Trees leaned in over his right side, and he expected, in shade, to find a breath of cooler air. Surprise hit him; there was no cooler air. The bank of shadow he was in delivered the same burning glare of heat as the open road free of shadow or shade. This, he knew, was doubt and non-acceptance rearing its head. Many times, with the resonance, the calling, at him, he had felt the same way, as if inadequate, unworthy of what was coming.

John Wellborn, his old and loyal friend, came up alongside him, head crouched, on his run, legs still ramming their piston power. John was merely making a bodily announcement, saying nothing, but broadcasting alertness, as if to say, "Knock, do you know what you're up to?" There had been long nights for them when they had no need of talk, the stars best company or the wind in the pines on a fishing trip, or the quiet summation the way some special days with friends find their end.

Knock recalled how he had almost told John one night

about the sounds in his ears, the ringing, the music, the endless call from an unknown place. He remembered, too well, how feeble, hysterical and unbelievable it would have sounded. On John's face there had been some kind of expectation, awaiting an explanation as to what had controlled much of Knock's attention and thinking all through their bonding years. But John was the kind of friend who knew better than ask. He simply trusted Knock. Here again, neither warning nor declaration was needed.

Paris Gallber orated to reporters and cameramen from three news vans alongside the road. Still astride his bike and leaning on a guardrail, his hands flew in the air and pointed back down the road as if someone was drowning and they weren't looking at the right spot. "Oh, I'll finish my ride, that's for sure, but I am not taking any shortcut, nor leading my teammates on a wild goose chase down any lonely and forgotten road. You can bet on that! I don't know what happened to the team captain. Like that," and he snapped his fingers, "he plunged down that side road and they all followed him, like he was the Pied Piper for god's sake. The Pied Piper! Can you imagine that! Can you?" And then, the way one might seem to be adjusting his anger, the subtle invasion of an ironic stiletto came into play. "I really don't know what you guys are going to do with all of this."

At that precise moment the lifelong calling from elsewhere in the universe, whether demonic or godlike, came with unerring clarity to Knock Craften as John Wellborn slowed back into the pack of riders.

Knock's gaze swept down the long grade of that unknown road, the shade and shadows suddenly cooler, the trees thicker on one side and a corral fence of split rails leaping away on his left side, leading perhaps a hundred yards downhill to the simple whiteness of a

196

small house. On a short piece of lawn he saw a little boy, about five, on a tricycle, a cowboy hat atop his head, possibly a future biker in the event he was now in. Knock hoped that cancer would never touch this child. Too many had he seen, too few could he help, and this ride was the only way he could help, if indeed he hadn't screwed it up. He wondered if this youngster was a sign, a very special Pedal Partner from out of the blue.

Then, materializing from the opposite end of the road, a dark automobile pulled up beside the child. A man got out, his body language precisely clear to Knock Craften who detected a sense of urgency and suspicion about how the man moved warily, craftily, slyly. In a flicker, the man was beside the child, and lifted him off his tricycle. The cowboy hat fell to the ground, and long blonde hair was loosed, revealing a little girl who he firmly clutched and raced back to his car.

On a side road, a forgotten road, leading his team away from their sworn and vouchsafed objective, Knock Craften was immediately in possession of that which had been coming to him all his life. He screamed, "John!" and pointed down the road. The tussling child in the man's arms was clearly visible, now a mere forty yards away, her legs and arms waving and kicking, the terror of her screams filling the shade and the shadows of the roadway. John Wellborn yelled out in alarm and anger. Legs pumping wildly, anger loose and free, the rigors of the long ride from Sturbridge lost in a fraction of a second, Knock, John and the team zipped down the road and before that dread man could wrestle the struggling child into the car, even as the child's mother raced across the short span of lawn, Team Vanish was all over him.

They held him in place for the police who came in minutes from a traffic spot on the main road. John

Wellborn sat astride his chest the whole while, a few times threatening the man that he'd thoroughly pummel him again. The news press, replying to their radio alerts, were in hot pursuit behind the authorities.

Paris Gallber, back on the main route, really had no idea what the newsmen were going to do with the story of Knock Craften, bike rider, and his teammates of Team Vanish.

As the man was led away in handcuffs, John noticed Knock crouched, talking to the little girl and her mother. He smiled and remounted his bike. His old pal, once safely at the end of this journey, would not be long from telling him secrets.

§ § §

Eleven years retired, Tom Sheehan operates with his partner, Larry Bucaria, Newwriters.com, helping writers find publishing space.

He is co-editor of the sold-out "A Gathering of Memories, Saugus 1900-2000," a nostalgic and historical 452-page look at his hometown, Saugus, MA, just north of Boston. Their committee borrowed $60,000 to print the book and paid it off five weeks after receipt of books.

He has work in Paumanok Review, 3amMagazine, Small Spiral Notebook, Dakota House, Stirring, Samsara, Comrades, Split Shot, Melange, Red River, Nefarious, Carnelian, New Works Review, Eclectica, Slow Trains, Clackamas Review, etc.

A print novel, "Vigilantes East," has just been released by Publish America, and another, "An Accountable

Death," is serialized on 3amMagazine.

He has been nominated for Pushcart Prize XXVII and awarded a 2001 Silver Rose Award for Excellence in the Art of the Short Story by American Renaissance for the Twenty-first Century (ART).

This poem is from a poetry manuscript, "This Rare Earth and Other Flights," of which more than 50 poems have appeared in print or on electronic sites.

THE MAN WITH THE BLUE THROAT

by Gary Cadwallader

My name is Cheal. I cull the herd.

Ravi Jodphur stares out the bus window every morning looking for me as I appear to him, and only him. I dress well, but the skin at my throat is blue. Sometimes he thinks he should buy a gun, sometimes he thinks that it is no use, sometimes he believes he is insane.

Today I hide from him and he gets off the bus in front of his building where he takes the elevator to the twelfth floor and sets his briefcase down on the large table beside his computer. He makes a circle on the wall calendar. Circles are good. Circles are clear days. X's mean he's seen the man with the blue throat. Last week there were two X's. This week there are four.

At lunch, he takes the sack his wife packed lovingly and the Pepsi he buys from the machine and goes down to the sidewalk. When he's finished, he walks into the alley beside his building and pitches his trash in the green dumpster. He leaves five dollars for the man living in the alley.

Such a good man - Ravi Jodphur. Such a pity.

An old man lives in the alley. He has a box with his name on it. The old man wrote "Hoagie Joagie" all over the big cardboard box that used to say "Kenmore Refrigerator". And then he wrote, "Feed me." The box is behind the dumpster and a pile of garbage bags. On one side of the alley there is an empty pool hall reminding Ravi of a painting he once saw of gaunt people sitting in puddles of lamplight.

The old man wears *all* his clothes in layers. His shoes have cardboard on the inside. Hoagie Joagie carries a snow shovel in the summer and walks in the street yelling at cars. "Damn you, get out of my way." And he shovels trash up on the sidewalk so that the curb is always clean.

When he's tired, Hoagie Joagie drags the shovel behind him. It is deadly looking -- sharp and jagged on the end -- and makes strange scraping sounds as he walks. You can hear him coming for blocks.

Ravi speaks to him. "How's it going?" Hoagie Joagie fixes a dead looking eye on Ravi and points to his shoes. "The cardboard keeps out the slithery snakes that live under the earth writhing in sexual frenzy."

"There are no snakes," Ravi says, looking at the solid concrete of the alley.

"At night teenagers shine flashlights in my box and kick the sides."

"I believe you," Ravi says and reachs out to touch the man.

Hoagie Joagie flinchs away.

*

Going home Ravi gets off the 63rd St. bus and sees me sitting quietly in a red swing, with my Pierre Cardin suit and wrinkly blue neck . Ravi stumbles down the steps and drops his black leather briefcase. The bus -- it's sides covered with zebras and the words, VISIT THE ZOO - squashes the work he's brought home with a crack and a puff of white papers.

Ravi pulls up the sleeve of his pure wool suit and with

shaking hands, fishes for his briefcase in a curbside puddle. Six feet behind him is a wire fence, beyond that, a childless playground. Ravi feels me watching, but when he turns around the playground is deserted.

He slips off the curb and slices his knee. He walks home with torn pant legs and wet shoes.

In India his parents still worship many gods and bathe ecstatically in a greasy brown river. As a child, Ravi most feared Shiva, the god of destruction. Seeing a blue throated man, one of Shiva's incarnations, means drastic change, and he longs to make a quick sacrifice to the old gods.

Instead he crosses himself as the missionaries have taught him and counts his blessings. He has a beautiful blonde wife and a new brick home. He has a job in America that pays more than his father will earn this decade. He has two bright children that are the loves of his life.

And, as he thinks of them, panic forces him into a sloppy, foot slapping run.

Lights flash through the iron gate as he turns the last corner. There is his house, towering like an English castle. There is his driveway, bent in a semi-circle and coming back to the street, there the young trees he's planted by hand, all bathed in an eerie wash of red and blue.

Lights flash across the green yard, then across his face, as he wanders towards the house. A sudden wind makes his hair stand up and he smells blood.

Men in black uniforms with shiny badges block him with their arms. "Stay back. You don't want to see what she did," they say as more men, this time in white, begin to wheel out the small bodies.

He catches a glimpse of his wife chained like an animal. She is nude. She is covered with blood. Inhuman eyes stare at him. The eyes say it is his fault and he thinks of a tiger that he'd once seen eating a boy.

A policeman wraps a blue blanket around her as she howls, trying to clutch it to her throat.

They will not let him speak to her. He follows the ambulance as the reality of death sets in. Tears well up, slide down his cheeks and wet his suit. He cannot stand the silence and reaches for the radio. He hesitates. What might they play that could break his heart? He drives over a curb. The walk into the emergency room is like a swim upstream.

He signs papers in a shaky hand and nurses nod in speechless sympathy.

When all is done, he walks away ignoring the policeman who offers to drive him home. He ignores his own car, not caring if he ever sees it again. It is after midnight. The air is humid and he wanders in the darkness with a vision of his wife gone insane. There is no difference between the darkness here and the darkness of the jungle.

He passes the alley by his work and hears the old man gibbering to himself. "I'm the Hoagie Joagie," the man says in a watery, rattling voice. "I'm the Hoagie Joagie and you can't get away."

Ravi walks into the alley. A green dumpster is to his left, piles of garbage bags to his right, carrying the smell of rotted meat and slippery cabbage. Behind them is a refrigerator box lying on its side. He hears muffled sounds from inside. Ravi speaks to the box. "My wife killed our children tonight."

The box goes quiet.

"Did you hear what I said? She killed them." Ravi kicks the box and a ragged man squirms free and stares at him with red frightened eyes. "Shiva?"

The old man humps away like a gorilla, huffing and drooling. His smell, worse then the garbage, reaches Ravi and makes him gag. The man of rags disappears around a corner leaving one shoe behind.

"I'm going crazy," Ravi says and leaves twenty dollars on the cardboard box.

Ravi turns away from the alley and into the brightly-lit street. He walks past a Catholic church and spits on the door. "What god are you," he says, "who would let this happen?" He beats on the door but no one answers.

He is nearly home. It is two in the morning. The wind stops and the only sounds are made by his own shuffling feet. As he nears the bus stop where he's stood every morning he hears the squeak-squawk of the chains holding up the child's red swing.

He stares straight ahead. Beads of sweat slide down his collar. Then it occurs to him that there is nothing left to lose.

He turns around very afraid, but standing straight.

"Shall I do more?" I ask in a whisper. My voice is soft and clear, but I know it feels like cold sweat down his back. Ravi watches me twist in the swing like a child.

"Isn't this enough?" Ravi stammers.

I have to laugh at his innocence.

"What do you want from me?"

I sit quietly for a moment, staring at Ravi and pausing so when he finally hears me he'll be devastated. "Kill the Hoagie Joagie."

"That old bum?" Ravi's eyes widen. "What has he to do with me?"

"Kill the Hoagie Joagie and I will give everything back. Your wife's sanity. Your children safe in their beds."

"No. You're not Shiva. I don't know what you are. Nothing I've ever heard of, but you're no god."

I nod. He's close. "Maybe not, but I can give you what you want."

Ravi hesitates. "Bring them back first."

I have him now. Bargaining with me rarely works out.

I give him a dazzling smile, white teeth gleaming, prepping him like a nurse shaving his genitals and then I let his wife appear in the playground in a long blood red dress. His children are with her laughing and holding her hands.

"Do it for us," she says. "Bring us back safe."

I make them disappear.

Ravi doesn't speak. He walks back the way he's come, finding his own footsteps like a tiger follows a well-worn trail. He shakes his head, "No, no, no." Then he cries, "But I must."

He argues with himself like a madman until he finds the alley. Mumbles and curses come from behind the pile of garbage like the rhythmic beating of drums.

Hoagie Joagie. Hoagie Joagie! HOAGIE JOAGIE!!

Ravi enters the shadows of the alley.

*

As dawn breaks, Ravi walks past his car in the driveway and opens his front door. He can hear his wife in the kitchen. She sings quietly and her voice is sweet. He can hear water being poured into the coffee maker.

There is a muffled scraping sound as his feet sink into the carpet. He looks into the children's room and sees them sleeping. Their breath moves the blankets up and down and he sighs.

Ravi leaves bloody footprints as he walks to the kitchen. Just before his wife turns around and starts screaming at the sprays of blood across his face, Ravi says, "I chopped off his head."

As his wife screams, her throat turns blue. Ravi's hefts Hoagie Joagie's shovel and swings it in a bright silver arc.

§ § §

Gary Cadwallader lives with his beautiful wife in Kansas City, Missouri, where they raise horses. His short stories and flash fiction have appeared in Literary Potpourri, Flashquake, InterText, The Palace of Reason, Insolent Rudder, and the Phone-Book. He has a new flash coming to Canter Magazine.

Given a chance, he'd catch unicorns for a living, paint tuxedos on penguins, or, he could write.... Just in case, he keeps his day job.

THE DEBT

by Rebecca Marshall-Courtois

Marco is surrounded by caged souls. Wherever he aims his flashlight, eyes reflect back at him. They peer out at him from corners, and pause to blink at him lethargically. The pacing paws of big cats offer a humble drumbeat in counter-point to the snores of their cubs. Wolves belt out hungry cries. Bears growl the blues. Birds squawk, owls hoot, monkeys chat, and beavers clap tails on man-made water holes. And from Marco's belt loop, dangling keys jingle in time.

The nightshift at the zoo isn't all that different from his previous job as prison guard. It has advantages though. For one, he doesn't have to deal with colleagues. The first thing he did after changing jobs was name the animals as if they were the old inmates. There's a turtle who has Derikson's neck, a snake who lisps like that skinny kid Alberto, and an old bear who lies around farting just like Barry from the East Wing. And just like prison, he prefers to talk with Curtis. The Canadian wolf is the image of his old best friend. The wolf really listens. After all, they're buddies. For life. "Idiots, all of them ! Told me I was too buddy-buddy with you," Marco complains to Curtis. "Just because I didn't fit in with the rest!"

Inmates made perfect conversationalists - they had little to say, lots of time to listen, nowhere to go if they grew tired of him. Curtis even seemed to enjoy listening to his monologues. A graying black man with a purple slug of a bottom lip that he pulled into a snarl of a smile whenever Marco came around to his cell, Curtis was different. The others used to spit and curse at Marco, daring him to take a step closer to their cells, but Curtis had always respected him. Thanks to Curtis, they started treating Marco differently, and even made an effort to chat with him on occasion. But they were just mocking him, Marco knew. Curtis was the only one he could count on.

The animals aren't all that different. Marco is no longer sure where he works or with whom he chats - everything has somehow blurred together in his mind. It's easier that way. "It ain't my fault they fired me, Curtis," he tells the wolf. "Bunch of jerks! Weren't for them, you and me would be living it up, huh? Never liked any of those guys. Offered me three months severance pay. I told them to keep it. Don't need it anyway. I got me one million, five hundred forty-six thousand, two hundred and fifty-three dollars stashed away for my early retirement, huh, Curtis ole boy? Thanks to you, of course. Don't worry - I haven't forgotten about your share, buddy! And my promise. Just got to get me a plan, you know?"

The wolf glances at him. Just the edge of his mouth curves upward, exposing iridescent slivers of teeth.

"You know, Curtis, sometimes I wish I'd never met you." Marco feels an old familiar shiver, looking into the icy eyes of the animal.

The wolf turns, walks to the wall and then turns to face him again. His ears remain pointed and alert, but his expression is one of indifferent tolerance. After a moment, the wolf turns away from him again and paces back toward the wall he's come from. The tip of his tail twitches from left to right accentuating the animal's snub stride. "Attitude," the inmates called it. Marco has never mastered it.

"I know, I know, I owe you. We have a deal," Marco stammers. "Buddies are supposed to take care of each other, right? Just like you said. You'll be getting out of here one of these days, and we'll be all set." He watches the wolf guarding his territory as if he has something to lose. "All my life I wanted to be rich, to have enough money to put my feet up and quit the nightshift," he says, chuckling. "But I guess my body's gotten used to sleeping all day and working all night. Can't sleep until the dawn creeps up on me. And what would I do all night if I didn't work, huh? Watch fishing programs? Who would I talk to, huh?"

Marco lets out a nervous laugh and the wolf takes a seat to pant at him. A string of spittle dangles from his mouth, and the silver-tinged fur on his back feathers up into spikes. But the smile never fades from the canine's face.

"Can't help thinking about things--about that night. Haunts me. I know you're right - I owed you. I know that buddies like us, buddies for life, have to help each other out, and that sometimes that means we've got to do things we might not really feel like doing. I understand, and I was there for you, right? Didn't I do good? I know a perfect crime means you leave no traces. And, like you said, he was a good-for-nothing guy anyway. We ended his misery, and ended ours. But funny thing is, I can't bring myself to spend a dime of that dough. Still stashed in the Chevy's trunk growing mold. Maybe I just need company, huh? Someone to travel with, dine with, you know? When you get out, we'll be living it up. Just like you promised, huh Curtis?"

But Curtis has been sentenced to life. Marco's pulse rises to his ears. The incessant pounding flushes out all other sounds. He shakes his head, wishing he could shut it off.

"It ain't fair, huh? Me out here and you, well,-- but you'll get out of here. I'll take you over to that fancy French place," Marco tells him. "That joint upstate. Chez

Georgette. Get us some kind of shrimp thing in pastry with a buttery sauce as a starter, then roast duck. The only thing is I'd want to eat that bird with my fingers and lick off the sauce. Can't do that in a place like that. I know you don't go for that French stuff though. You'd want one of those thick slabs of meat. Prime Rib. Soon we'll be living it up. Promise you! I just got to find that plan, a perfect plan. The thing is, Curtis, I just can't do what I did that night. Never again."

The wolf lifts the corner of his upper lip and Marco's flashlight catches his teeth. They gleam. Curtis' shadow is tripled, extending darker monstrous versions of the wolf into the trees beyond his den. It's like a pack of angry Curtises, ghosts of formerly betrayed souls, are waiting for him to come clean. Marco aims his flashlight at his feet and the wolf circles his way into a ball in the corner of the den.

"Sweet dreams, buddy," Marco says with a wave. The wolf raises his head, licks his chops contentedly and then settles back down again. Marco notices how lazy the old guy has become. Canadian wolves are supposed to hunt at night - it is written on the sign in front of Curtis's cage. Above the description a photograph of a slick cousin of Curtis' is lacquered onto the wood. The wolf is walking majestically through a snowy forest, grinning a Curtis grin at the photographer.

"Freedom," Marco says to the sky. Marco's never felt free. He supposes he was once, before that July night when Curtis told him, "I like you, Marco. You and me could have been buddies, you know, out there? That's why I stick up for you when the other guys get on your case. I help you out, you know. But I'd like to do more for you. Buddies do that, don't they? Help each other out."

Marco laughed at this.

"I'm serious. You got it hard, I know. You deserve better for yourself." And Curtis came to the bars and twitched his head to let Marco know he was to come closer. "Psst, buddy?" Curtis said. "How'd you like a sure fire plan? Big bucks. You can't lose. You could quit this dead-end job, take off to see the world?"

"Oh, come on, Curtis. I never even stole a stick a gum as a kid. Besides, look where your plans got you?"

"This is different. No risk involved. But you aren't up to it, I guess. Yeah, you too honest. A good boy. Look where it's gotten you? You're not right for this job, you know? Guys like you get beat up in places like this. Killed. They'll be after you, you know. In a couple of years time. When they get out. They'll find you. They always do. And then, who's going to be around to protect you, huh? Face it, you aren't much better off than me. But I thought we were buddies. It's no big deal. I understand. You don't need me, right?"

"So what's this plan?"

"I know this guy. Used to work with him. Used to be a buddy, like you. Betrayed me." Curtis spit into the corner of his cell. "He's out there, rich and happy, and here I am, paying for the both of us."

"You want me to talk to him?"

Curtis' laugh came from his gut, and exploded on the cement, rattling the bars and Marco's nerves. "You too good, buddy. You a real buddy. Trust, you see, it's all about trust. Two things can kill a guy - greed and betrayal. This guy got both. Got to put him out of his misery."

"You don't,--"

"Hey, buddy. It's my dough. I'm being nice. Figure a deal's a deal. I help you out, you help me out. And if you help me out, I give you half. We share, like buddies should. It's come time to set things right, is all. We take care of each other. Right? We're buddies, aren't we?"

A week later, Marco came face to face with death. Not his own, although he often wonders.

A man gets this look on his face when he knows he's done - actually it's a series of looks. First, his eyes bulge, his mouth rounds out. And then, muscles relax and a peace comes over that same face - wrinkles disappear, lids grow lazy. At night when Marco is at that in-between stage, almost asleep but still alert, he remembers that guy's face. Marco will never forget the look he had. Not once in his life has Marco ever felt the way that man seemed to feel before Marco's finger curled around the trigger. It was almost as though the guy found peace in the last seconds of his life - the way Marco feels just before he finally nods off. Things make sense to Marco then, in that semi-conscious state. Only then.

"Two things can kill a man," Marco repeats to himself over and over. "Betrayal and greed."

Marco spends the rest of his shift wandering from cage to cage, but there's no escaping his own imprisoned soul. The moon is just a sliver shy of being full. Its spectral glow alters colors. It looks as though a grayish violet dust has been sprinkled over everything. Even the skin on Marco's hands has been coated with it. They glitter an eerie shade of dusk, of death. Tomorrow the moon will be full.

Marco hates full moon shifts. Kids climb the fence on dares when the moon's full, disrupting the already anxious animals. And some animals break out of their cages. Not the dangerous ones of course, not the high security inmates, but the birds, for one. Like classy babes out on the town, they ruffle their feathers at Marco to tease him and make him run circles after them all night. Just before dawn, they slip back into their cages to gaze at Marco, their gentle eyes bewildered at the sight of him struggling to catch his breath. One night, his anger got loose, that dark stranger that dwelled in him was so fed up with their antics and squawking that he tossed an innocent, stick-legged flamingo into the tiger cage. Better than cable TV, that show. But he knew he shouldn't make a habit of it - it might cost him his job.

And then what would he do all night? Let his mind wander to those places, down roads that come full circle again and again? He circles around the cages again. He can feel the tension approaching. The air the night before a full autumn moon hurts when you inhale a big burst of it, as if it were filled with suspended bits of ice that embed themselves in the sides of your lungs. This is something that happens, he's heard, in parts of Canada.

Everything feels like that Canadian air - suspended and frozen. Odors linger. That decaying stench of wild beast and excrement encompasses him. The prison corridors had the same smell to them, and he remembers how the inmates hung arms and noses through the bars of the windows to try to escape it.

The animals are as stilled as the air. Most of them. Other things twitch in the shadows. They're out there. Marco can smell their sour coffee breath on the back of his neck. He won't run. He grips onto his flashlight to steady it, and watches the shadows out of the corner of his eyes. But they're tricky rascals, flitting away just when he turns around. Marco swings back around to

214

Curtis' cage, but he finds him curled up in the corner of his shack. "Sleep tight, buddy," Marco whispers. "Sweet dreams," he whispers a bit louder, hoping to wake Curtis up, but Curtis doesn't move. Marco knows better than to wake Curtis up on purpose.

The gentle sway of sleepers breathing is ominous, forewarning. Marco guzzles coffee. His senses wake up more than his body. Ideas come to him. Rather than shake them off, he dwells on them. This is what happens to him when he is about to fall asleep. But instead of sleeping, he remains locked in this in-between phase when everything seems plausible and where things have a strange way of connecting. And around and around he runs. Until he begins to see a side road that he's never noticed before. It may be a dead end, but it's an end, an end to all this circling, in a world that stands still, waiting.

The next night, when the sky turns an ashy violet and the moon lights everything up like a flood light, Marco retrieves the duffle bags full of cash from the trunk of his old Chevy and goes to work. The bags bring to his office an odor of mold and stale tobacco that they've sponged up over the years. Marco uses them as footrests and watches the surveillance cameras for a spell, pounding slugs of a fifth of Scotch he'd added to one of the bags. When he leans back in his swivel chair far enough, he has a clear view of that ball of wax stuck in the sky. He would have liked to have been Armstrong, he thinks then, imagining what it would be like to be weightless. Would it feel like falling in a dream? That's bliss. He takes another slug of Scotch, in search of similar sensations. Marco lugs the two bags and the bottle down the path, one last circle. There's no need for the flashlight - the moon lights the way. The noise is unyielding. Yelps and yaps compete with one another in different octaves.

Marco pauses by the lion cage to take another sip of Scotch. "Benny boy!" he lifts the drink to the feline who stops pacing and takes a seat in front of Marco. "How's the wife?"

The lioness sneers at Marco from the back of the cage. Benny gazes back complacently. "I can relate, I sure can relate!"

"Arrrrrroowww!" Benny grumbles.

"Here's to you, Benny!" he shouts, toasting his companion. "Best of luck."

Marco moves on. Now too drunk and tired to carry the bags, he finishes off the Scotch and tosses the empty bottle at one of the bears. Then he drags the duffle bags along by the straps. When he arrives before Curtis's den, the bear's enraged growl still lingers. He spots movement in the trees, and the glow of Curtis' roommates' eyes before they dart away.

But Curtis is waiting for him, his winter coat fluffed, his ears alert, his muscles flexed and his eyes piercing.

"It's pay back time, ole buddy," he tells the wolf.

The animal raises his snout in acknowledgement.

Marco flings the first bag over the fence and it lands with a burst at the bottom of the cage. The wolf approaches the bag, bats a paw at it, then takes a few steps back, approaches it again and sniffs at it. Satisfied, the wolf emits a low gurgle before snatching it up in his teeth and tossing the bag into his shack.

"I went to the funeral, buddy. I know, I know. You told me not to. No one saw me though. I shouldn't have been there. That guy you told me I'd put out of his misery? He had a wife, kids. Why didn't you tell me that?"

Curtis pauses to glance at him before sinking his teeth back into the duffle bag.

Marco is still standing on the ledge, his sneakers tucked under the fence, his head nestled between two bars at the top of the fence. He has seen children stand like this, on his rare off-duty visits to the zoo. It's unnerving but actually, there isn't much risk involved. A window of Plexiglas still separates Marco and Curtis.

He's a good sport that Curtis, Marco thinks. He puts on quite the show by shredding the bag, scattering the ground and surrounding brush with hundred dollar bills. From where he stands, Marco can smell that tingly odor of money that has somehow remained fresh after all those years in the back of the Chevy. But then, he's never so much as unzipped the bags. He hopes they're all watching. He's sure they're there, hiding a bit further back in the brush tonight. That'll show them. They'll think twice about him, regret how they all treated him. He laughs.

Marco tosses the other bag over the Plexiglas and the wolf looks up at him. For but an instant, Marco is allowed the thrill of catching Curtis off guard. He watches the wolf as he calculates the scene, the brief expression of confusion overtaking that familiar austerity. Curtis prances back to the front of the cage, and takes a seat just below Marco's feet, beckoning him.

Marco makes his way over the bars. With his face plastered against the Plexiglas, his Scotch scented breath dizzies him. Or perhaps it is seeing just how steep that drop-off is that makes his head spin. The bottom of the cage is maybe eight or ten feet deeper than the walkway surrounding it. Safety codes about dangerous animals, Marco knows. They never had codes like that at the prison - those guys could reach between the bars and grab him if he got too close.

Underneath him, Curtis flashes him his best puppy dog smile and goes about washing his paws. But his pet-like behavior does nothing to overcome the effect the smells have on Marco. When his chin hooks over the top of the Plexiglas, he is taken aback. It is as if death has already occurred down there. Flies buzz around Curtis's leftovers, uncooked and partially decomposed, at the far side of the cage. Curtis has been saving his appetite for prime rib. He's always known that the wolf understood.

"Betrayal and greed, you said, buddy, can kill a man. Remember?" Marco says, struggling to pull his leg over the slippery barrier. "But buddy, there are more than two things that can kill a man and there's more than one way to kill him." The wolf offers Marco one last crooked smile.

§ § §

Rebecca Marshall-Courtois left Westchester, New York behind when she fell in love with her French boss twelve years ago. She now lives in Buxerolles, the French equivalent of modern suburbia. She has three young daughters and works as a college English teacher and freelance translator while completing her postgraduate studies in literature.

Despite her hectic schedule, she always finds time to write and run, her two addictions. Her fiction has recently appeared in Love Words, The Sidewalk's End, Moondance and E2K.

FLASH FICTION

LADY GODIVA SHOWERS IN THE DARK

by Emily Gaskin

He perches on the showerhead, a camera eye
penetrating a gap in rough tile. He wants to take a
picture of the galaxy that he's in, but he's afraid of
steam fogging up the lens.

He has already envisioned her: the Milky Way, a perfect
spiral -- slender, symmetrical, arms like delicate white
scarves wind-milling through black liquid space. He
wonders if his flash will work.

The woman showers without a light. Black steam licks
her naked body as her hands, silken with soap, work
over her muscles and folds. She opens her lips to the
water, and fire drowns her throat. It overflows her
mouth, cascading down her body, snaking around her
navel and down the insides of her thighs to collect in a
pool at her feet, which are large and cover the drain.

He wonders why she showers alone, without him, in the
dark. The camera noses further into the shadows,
twisting in focus with a faint, mechanical hiss. Why
enforce his ignorance? Why bind his perspective to the
inside, a helpless view outward through a veil of astral
dust?

Dim, watery stars drip from her lashes. The glassy walls
of her eyes meet the darkness -- reflecting, oblivious.
Delighting in the acoustics of inner spaces, she sings a
wordless aria, the intimate lore of her body. It rings out
too high, interrupted, repeating -- the idiosyncratic
Doppler shifting chirps of galactic song. In the
labyrinthine bones of his inner ear, her music rebounds
like an infinite aural signature.

She massages balsam into her hair, twisting the lengths in her fingers. Each unfurled curl, it seems to him, measures the fate of one more world in her assembly of satellites and luminous haze. One more spinning, fetal ball clinging to a deterministic orbit in a dance beyond its comprehension.

He commits to the guesswork of focus in darkness and takes his picture -- of what, he is not sure. The flash strobes in steam and water. The camera's pupil widens.

She whirls. Her hair flares out in strands of phosphorescent pearls, and she collapses. Her song dissolving into a wail, she spirals down the drain -- a trail of foam and steam. The madness of the black hole, then silence.

The camera eye falls back. He climbs down, sweaty and satisfied. In the solitude of his darkroom, the picture develops nicely -- a map and hymn of the slender, the symmetrical, the perfect spiral. He congratulates himself, reveling in the triumph of rendering the impossible. In his hands he holds the world outside the womb.

He enlarges the photograph and frames it on the wall above their empty bed. He shrinks it down to pocket size and carries it in his wallet, thinking to show it to friends, colleagues, strangers at the bus stop -- anyone who would dare to look.

Later, exhausted, he tries to take a shower -- cold, this time, and with the light on. Water rises to his ankles. He stoops and finds the drain clogged with long, twisting hair.

§ § §

Emily Gaskin wishes she took better astrophotographs, but will settle instead for consistently good personal hygiene. Her most recent work can be found in Strange Horizons, Ideomancer, and the upcoming Dust Devil anthology.

SATISFACTION GUARANTEED

by Mike Whitney

A disembodied female voice was singing that love will keep us together. Her perky vocal was briefly interrupted for a price check on vanilla yogurt by the cashier on register five.

Food Crest assistant manager trainee Bill Kincaid walked into Randall Overton's office just as the manager jammed his knee hard into the customer's stomach. Shrink-wrapped steaks fell from the man's leather jacket, smacking the concrete floor with the stinging snap of wet towel on bare skin. He spun slowly as the air rushed out of him. His outstretched arm hit the desk phone, knocking it to the floor. The man collapsed to his knees beside the desk hugging his arms about him.

Bill felt a vein pulse in his left temple. Face flushed, the store manager looked at him "I caught this boy stuffing his coat with New York strips. Boy, those are MY steaks until you pay for them!"

The manager kicked at the man, who rolled away, huffing to catch his breath. He looked up at Overton with bloodshot eyes. Kincaid started to speak; Overton glared a warning at him. The manager's big belly was taut against the buttoned red blazer with the company slogan over the handkerchief pocket: *Food Crest - Satisfaction Guaranteed.* The customer got to his knees, and Overton turned to him. "You're going to jail, boy. You hear me? I'll tell the cops I caught you boosting my beef and you tried to get away, so I had to DETAIN you."

The man said nothing as he got slowly to his feet, eyes

riveted on Overton. Bill picked the phone off the floor, listened for a dial tone. The vein in his forehead throbbed rapidly. "The phone is dead, sir. I'll call from Customer Service."

"Make it quick."

"Right."

As he started out the door, Bill saw the man stoop to pick up the packages. He took a step towards Overton. "Here's your meat, my man."

His voice was low, but carried clearly through the small office.

Bill closed the office door and slowly walked to Customer Service at the opposite end of the large store. Behind him, he could hear the man's rising voice as he passed Frozen Foods.

"I SAID, don't you want your meat, Mister Manager Man?"

Bill hummed along with the store speakers as he strolled, while Gordon Lightfoot sang if you could read my mind.

§ § §

Born in Chicago, now lurking in the North Carolina hills, Mike Whitney has been self-medicating with short stories and songs since 1954, when a play he wrote in class at ten was produced for local radio.

In 1970, Whitney began performing popular and

225

original music in restaurants, clubs and coffeehouses. This behavior continues today. He and his wife are owned by two cats and the bank in Hayesville.

This is Mike's first published story.

LULLING

by Margetty Coe

A wave broke and she turned her back and crouched
down, waiting. Tumbling water reached her, churning
her hair and shivering along her skin. She leaned into it,
let her arms and legs lift and loosen in the surge. Then
the flow eased, releasing her. She sank back slowly,
heels digging into sand as the wave sucked out and
streamed to deeper water.

She turned to face the waves again and curled herself.
The wash licked at her chin, her toes brushed the
bottom. Between them, her body -- a formless,
unfamiliar weight, carried on the current's push-pull. A
new set glided forward, two small swells and then a
larger one; she must watch and be ready for the big
wave to break.

Even in shallow water she felt brave to let herself be
tangled by the surf. And then she thought, This isn't
real fear -- not like capsizing in a storm, or seeing a
child caught in a riptide -- but a taste of it. A hint.

When she was small a wave had grabbed her and
dragged her under. Water rushing all around her. No
air. No breath. For a long time afterward she feared the
ocean, as if it were a living creature, hungry, reaching
for her, its toothless fish-mouth gaping beneath the
quivering surface. She was afraid to go in above her
knees. After a time she recovered herself, by watching
other children, listening to their teasing, feeling
ashamed, till finally she shut her eyes, splashed in, and
found her way again.

Now the big wave began to break before she could
move to meet it. She dove into its rolling flank and right

away bumped the sand. She fought to keep below the tumult until the current ebbed. Then she looked up, drifting, to see a chaos of foamy streaks and ripples with pale lights flickering through.

Tired of wrestling with the waves, she ducked below the surf again to swim towards calmer water. With every stroke she stretched, cut through the surface, pushed swiftly forward. In the gentle swells beyond the break she stopped to rest. She floated, gazing up into an endless, empty sky.

For a moment there was nothing. The muffled beating of her heart. Drops sliding off her skin. Her thoughts a mist. And then a salt breeze off the open sea reached her, stirred the mist and shaped it into words: Do I want it? she asked herself.

On land she had shifted back and forth, from wanting to not wanting, each a cliff from which she must jump down to hard ground, and no climbing up again.

On land her worries had dug ruts behind her brow. But here beyond the breakers every moment brought new riffles, and froth blew off at once on the breeze. Out here the question floated over her, a bubble, a puzzle whose key might drift in on a wave.

A swell rose smoothly at her feet, lifted and rocked her the length of her body. She thought of all the swells that rolled across the ocean -- all the way across. She tilted her head to look toward the horizon. Low-lying billows flowed steadily as far as she could see.

No words formed. But she felt the baby rocking with her, within her, rocking in the wide sea. Her baby and herself, carried on the current that rolled from the horizon. She let her body ease then, closed her eyes and let her head tip back until her ears were covered and she heard a lulling drumbeat in the surf. Behind her the water piled up, heaved over, drove against the sand.

§ § §

Margetty Coe lives and works as a graphic designer and advertising writer in Philadelphia, PA. This is her first published story.

PHOTO ESSAY

THE CHILDREN OF GAMBIA

By Danny Verhasselt

233

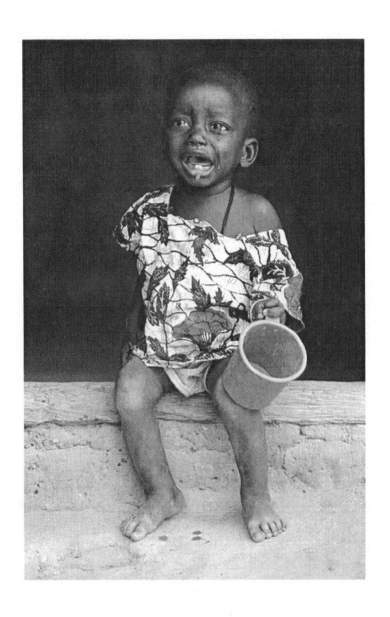

Danny Verhasselt (born 1961) lives in Denderwindeke, Belgium.

Since early childhood, he has been passionate about photography. He practices various styles of photography and has a degree in Art of Photography from the Academy of Arts, in Aalst.

Being a passionate traveler, his extensive travels around the world have lit the fire for travel-related photography. His images reveal the splendor of many cultural heritages and portraits of optimistic people, the world around.

POETRY

BLUE RAVEN

by Michael Spring

the raven floats through the blue shadows
of pines and campfire smoke

I want to follow it
through the cool woods
above wet shale and ragged limestone
I want to find the boy
who ran out on me years ago --
the one who stole my passion
for puzzles and mazes --

the one I ignored until he slipped
out the window on a morning like today -- seeking

scrolls
hidden in caves -- maps
under the wings of birds -- songs
in small creeks

I intend to find him --
I will search every green shadow

in every canoe slumbering
in soft reeds on the lake --

I will trample uphill, over the gashed and cracked
skin of the mountain -- over bull snake
and scorpion stones --

I will use my eyes to scour the land like this raven
-- already I can hear the boy's laughter
and rocks skipping
off the top of rocks

§ § §

*Michael Spring lives in Corvallis, OR. He is currently
looking for rural property and ready to get muddy and
build a house with cob. But surrealism, hypersurrealism
and abstract expressionism will always cling to his
mind like poison oak does to his skin.*

*His poems have recently been published or are
forthcoming in Atlanta Review, Midwest Quarterly,
Literary Potpourri (on-line), Chiron Review, Black Bear
Review, Main Street Rag, m.a.g and Painted Moon
Quarterly (on-line). His chapbook, "Edge of Blue," is
currently seeking more readers (publisher can be
reached at: Siskipress@cs.com).*

EVERYTHING IS ALL SET

by Zev Levinson

Dreaming of the sun, old girl?
Dream of nothing but
as through the rickety gate is sky,
a thickening smear of love.

I once knew a dog who wagged her tail
to the rhythm of sunshine broken through leaves.
It was an old trick of the light,
a repeating stanza no one hears twice.

We can bleat, we can bray,
but nothing sounds from so far away
as your dreamland bark. Puts me in your picnic,
ragamuffin, tongue-loller, eye-winker.

You taste the shadows of an afternoon
like a sleeping bee recalls lilac,
having furrowed, long ago, a stray cluster.
This is the corner I long to rock in,

the side of the room cleaned by sunbeams.
I am through with dusting,
everything is all set, really.
Speaking of perfection, this late breeze.

§ § §

Zev Levinson lives behind the Redwood Curtain in Humboldt County, California. He teaches at Humboldt State University and College of the Redwoods, and to younger students through California Poets in the Schools. He wonders if he'll ever grow up.

A WOMAN, STANDING STILL

by Ward Kelley

A woman, stands still in the street,
in the night, at the end of a summer

storm . . . the rain has nearly stopped,
but a few dog-eye drops make quite

a substantial sound when they hit
the asphalt. She stares at the bedroom

window where you stand. As angry as
you are, you would still give her anything

except this argument, to know what her neck
smells like after this rain, after all that's been said.

§ § §

Ward Kelley has seen more than 1200 of his poems appear in journals world wide. A Pushcart Prize nominee, Kelley's publication credits include such journals as: Another Chicago Magazine, Rattle, Zuzu's Petals, Ginger Hill, Sunstone, Spillway, Pif, Whetstone, 2River View, Melic Review, Thunder Sandwich, The Animist, Offcourse, Potpourri and Skylark. He was the recipient of the Nassau Review Poetry Award for 2001.

Kelley is the author of two paperbacks: "histories of souls," a poetry collection, and "Divine Murder," a novel; he also has an epic poem, "comedy incarnate" on CD and CD ROM. His website is: www.wardkelly.com.

Chevy

by L.A. Seidensticker

as though driven up out of the cribbing sea, drawn out
of the lily-padding ocean with its lace curtain overtures and its white hands
starfishing small-of-the-back encouragement to the baby's breath scud and foam,
a fifty-two chevy, rear wheels nuzzled and licked by high tide
front wheels settled some into higher ground, you could kneel on the back seat
watch out the back window the aqua marine table of the Atlantic
pitch and glitter under the folded-arm guardianship of tropic sky;

hear the surfy mumble that is almost words you used to know
in a language before this dull one now that is always sounding in your own ears
like phrases scooped up from under a dead bush planted by a back fence,
ideas full of compost and dry rot, hydrated
here to murmurs and murky confidences in the waveless slop of the Sea of Abaco
against a ground-aspirin beach

with the chevy not bad rusted hauled up onto it, come
nose first out of the sea in good enough shape you'd think somebody'd cherry
its musty mohair upholstery, the sun-blasted dash, its original dirty washwater paint;
smelling inside no worse than graham crumbs and just-opened ice chest,
than steering wheel sweat, sundried rubber thongs
and the elastic bands of the sun shades old aunts wear.

there's a shadow-colored sweater spilled on the back seat
and on the dashboard, an eight-inch plastic statue of liberty
where Jesus or Our Lady might've kept the sharper look out.

§ § §

l.a. seidensticker lives in the northern California wine country, very fortunately, two miles of bad road from the pavement. Even before the fact, publication is disconcerting

DOGGED POEM

by Greg Bauder

Howling at paperboys
and letter carriers,
transporters of words,

it snarls and bites
at fat cats who collar
and kennel it

yet, unashamed,
it yelps
through time.

Barking, pissing
at the tree of life--
a poem is loose!

§ § §

Greg Bauder has a BA in English Literature from The University Of British Columbia, and he has published in many North American magazines, including U.S. publications such as Thought, Songs Of Innocence, Penny Dreadful, Glyph, Morbid Curiosity and Above And Below.

He is Assistant Editor to the Canadian magazine, Tickled By Thunder for which he has worked the past four years.

ESSAY

THROUGH ME TELL THE STORY

by Carolyn Holdsworth

"Sing in me, Muse, and through me tell the story." The
author has only one name but two epics. Uncertainty
exists about his birthplace, thought to be Ionia, an
ancient Greek colony on Asia Minor. Homer is believed
to have been blind. One name, one fact (his blindness,
perhaps), another fact (his birthplace, in dispute), two
epics (arguments abound here about whether the same
mind could have created both.)

Arguments abound. There are those who prefer his
Iliad, a concentrated masterpiece covering several
weeks of the Trojan War, a defining event for the
ancient Achaeans who crossed a sea, stormed a citadel,
destroyed a royal family, and took back the Greek
woman named Helen, the most beautiful woman in the
world, stolen from his host by the Trojan prince Paris in
a gross violation of the cultural conventions of
hospitality.

But the hero of this epic is not Helen's husband or her
lover. The hero of this epic is Achilles, its theme the
destruction that wrath can cause, its imagery of fire. In
the *Iliad,* we get the first portrayal in western literature
of the bureaucrat gone mad with power lust, of the
obsessive-compulsive who regrets too late his rashness,
of the capriciousness of an unkind fate.

Although more temperamentally akin to Achilles, a
warrior with limited survival skills, and although a
believer in the tragic view of life, I prefer that lying
vagabond, that cheater and deceiver, that contender,
Odysseus, the one who survives the dangerous comedy

of life. One motif in the *Odyssey* is the imagery of food, not fire. Perhaps it is for the contrast that I prefer Homer's "lesser" epic.

All of western literature begins with Homer. He is the wellspring. His works were used as educational tools for Greek youths. His works were copied--by Virgil in the *Aeneid* and through him to Dante's *The Divine Comedy*. Joyce copied him in *Ulysses* as did Tennyson in his poem of that name. Even "O Brother, Where Art Thou" copied Homer recently. One wonders whose, if anyone's, shoulders Homer stood upon. Virgil, Dante, Ovid, Milton, even that comedian Pope and that failed epic poet Williams stood on Homer's.

I have certainly wanted to stand there. I began a story that progressed episodically and included large dollops of the fantastic and a quest for home. A member of my writer's group, a musician, asked me, "What kind of book is this anyway?" Without thinking through my reply, I responded, "An epic." Gotcha, Homer snickers.

So what are the facts of Homer's life? His facts are his works. I believe that the same mind created both works because I am capable of low humor and occasional poignancy myself, of contradictions in my view of life. I believe he might have lived in Ionia because he had that objective view of the Greek culture's heroes, a view achieved only by a relative outsider.

I believe he was blind because of the way he treats Demodokus, the blind minstrel in the *Odyssey*. Homer has Odysseus say that all men owe honor to the poets. Odysseus gives Demodokus the finest cut of meat at a banquet after listening to Demodokus sing his tale of Troy. And when another minstrel thinks Odysseus is about to slay him, as he has slain over a hundred suitors for his wife's hand and has slain their unfaithful servants who abetted this outrage on his household, his wife, his son, and his honor, the minstrel first places his instrument (the lute) carefully on a table. If he is to be slain, he doesn't want his instrument damaged. That is a lesson only a poet would teach. That and the smell of blood, which stinks.

Homer's greatest contribution to my life is his relevance--the relevance of a man who orally composed in 800 B.C. (a date that is disputed) the stories of what happened in 1200 B. C. (if, as some argue, those events ever occurred at all). Did Troy exist? Heinrich Schliemann claims to have found Troy, with only a copy of Homer in his hand to guide him. But Schliemann lied about other things as well, such as his young Greek wife's wearing of Helen's recovered jewels. The photograph of Schliemann's Greek wife is lovely, as lies so often are.

Where is the relevance? one might ask. He was Greek; I am American. He wrote of warriors; I am a woman. He wrote of epic deeds affecting civilizations; I write of my husband, my children, and my doppelgangers.

But Homer gave us monsters, which certainly exist in today's headlines, like the flesh-eating Cyclops and Laistrygonians, killers; he gave us drug addicts in the Lotus Eaters, showed us the dangers of complacency, of failure to strive; he gave us Odysseus' grief at his inability to embrace his dead mother, impalpable, sifting through his grasping fingers like mist; he gave us Circe, that witch, that woman, whose magic could not dominate Odysseus but whose "flawless bed of love" held him captive for a year, his only failure in his quest; he gave us the disasters we bring willfully upon ourselves such as when Odysseus's crew eats the sacred cows of Helios, whose flesh moos and crawls and brings their deserved destruction; he gives us a patron goddess, Athena, who slows the night to prolong the love between Odysseus, returned home after twenty years of struggles, to his wife, Penelope, whom he compares to a sun-warmed beach, to my mind the most beautiful metaphor for marriage in all of literature. No, it's not fair that Odysseus slept with both Circe and Calypso, but yes, he returned to his wife and found her faithful. He did return. And there are other failures of this hero, this anti-hero, Odysseus. He was the one who chose to remain in the Cyclops' cave, where six men were eaten, squirming like puppies, their brains bashed out. In fact, all his crew members die; only Odysseus survives to return home. And Penelope does not recognize him when he returns; she does not welcome him into their marriage bed, their secret sign, until he has proved himself Odysseus.

I used to bring matches to class to have my students smell the sulphur of Zeus's lightning bolt when he destroys Odysseus' ship and crew. Homer smells and sees and hears.

I am not given to admiration. But I wish to stand upon Homer's shoulders, if I can get there, just to see his view of the human comedy.

§ § §

Carolyn Holdsworth has taught at six colleges and universities, and World Literature I and II were among her favorite classes to teach.

Cornell University Press published her scholarly edition on W. B. Yeats's manuscripts for The Wind Among the Reeds. She's also published essays on Yeats, Hopkins, and others. The essay above won first place in the Geneva I. Crook Memorial Award contest at the Arkansas Writer's Conference in June 2002.

MID MONTH SURPRISE

HALF OF A YELLOW SUN

by Chimamanda Ngozi Adichie

The Igbo say that a mature eagle feather will always remain spotless.
*

It was the kind of day in the middle of the rainy season when the sun felt like an orange flame placed close to my skin, yet it was raining, and I remembered when I was a child, when I would run around on days like this and sing songs about the dueling sun and rain, urging the sun to win. The lukewarm raindrops mixed with my sweat and ran down my face as I walked back to my hostel after the rally. I was still holding the placard that read *Remember the Massacres*, still marveling at my new -- at our new -- identity. It was late May, Ojukwu had just announced the secession, and we were no longer Nigerians. We were Biafrans.

When we gathered at the Freedom Square for the rally, thousands of us students shouted Igbo songs and swayed, river-like; somebody said that in the market outside our campus, the women were dancing, giving away groundnuts and mangoes. Nnamdi and I stood next to each other and our shoulders touched as we waved green dogonyaro branches and cardboard placards. Nnamdi's placard read *Secession Now*. Even though he was one of the student leaders, he chose to be with me in the crowd. The other leaders were in front carrying a coffin with NIGERIA written on it in white chalk. When they dug a shallow hole and buried the coffin, a cheer rose and snaked around the crowd, uniting us, elevating us, until it was one cheer, until we all became one.

I cheered loudly, although the coffin reminded me of Aunty Ifeka, Mama's half-sister, the woman whose breast I sucked because Mama's dried up after I was born. Aunty Ifeka was killed during the massacres in the North. So was Arize, her pregnant daughter. They must have cut open Arize's stomach and beheaded the baby first -- it was what they did to the pregnant women. I didn't tell Nnamdi that I was thinking of Aunty Ifeka and Arize again. Not because I had lost only two relatives while he had lost three uncles and six cousins. But because he would caress my face and say, "I've told you, don't dwell on the massacres. Isn't it why we seceded? Biafra is born! Dwell on that instead. We will turn our pain into a mighty nation, we will turn our pain into the pride of Africa."

Nnamdi was like that; sometimes I looked at him and saw what he would have been two hundred years before: an Igbo warrior leading his hamlet in battle (but only a fair battle), shouting and charging with his fire-warmed machete, returning with the most heads lolling on sticks.

I was in front of my hostel when the rain stopped; the sun had won the fight. Inside the lounge, crowds of girls were singing. Girls I had seen struggle at the water pump and hit each other with plastic buckets, girls who had cut holes in each other's bras as they hung out to dry, now held hands and sang. Instead of 'Nigeria we hail thee,' they sang, 'Biafra we hail thee.' I joined them, singing, clapping, talking. We did not mention the massacres, the way Igbos had been hunted house to house, pulled from where they crouched on trees, by bright-eyed people screaming Jihad, screaming *nyamiri, nyamiri*. Instead, we talked about Ojukwu, how his speeches brought tears to our eyes and goose bumps to our skin, how easily his charisma would stand out among other leaders -- Nkurumah would look like a

264

plastic doll next to him. "*Imakwa*, Biafra has more doctors and lawyers than all of Black Africa!" somebody said. "Ah, Biafra will save Africa!" another said. We laughed, deliriously proud of people we would never even know, people who a month ago did not have the 'ours' label as now.

We laughed more in the following weeks -- we laughed when our expatriate lecturers went back to Britain and India and America, because even if war came, it would take us only one week to crush Nigeria. We laughed at the Nigerian navy ships blocking our ports, because the blockade could not possibly last. We laughed as we gathered under the gmelina trees to discuss Biafra's future foreign policy, as we took down the 'University of Nigeria, Nsukka' sign and replaced it with 'University of Biafra, Nsukka.' Nnamdi hammered in the first nail. He was first, too, to join the Biafran Army, before the rest of his friends followed. I went with him to the Army enlistment office, which still smelled of fresh paint, to collect his uniform. He looked so broad-shouldered in it, so capable, and later, I did not let him take it all off, I held on to the grainy khaki shirt as he moved inside me.

My life -- our lives -- had taken on a sheen. A sheen like patent leather. We all felt as though it was liquid steel, instead of blood, that flowed through our veins, as though we could stand barefoot over red-hot embers.
*
The Igbo say -- who knows how water entered the stalk of a pumpkin?
*

I heard the guns from my hostel room. They sounded close, as though thunder was being funneled up from the lounge. Somebody was shouting outside with a loudspeaker. Evacuate now! Evacuate now! There was

265

the sound of feet, frenzied feet, in the hallway. I threw things in a suitcase, nearly forgot my underwear in the drawer. As I left the hostel, I saw a girl's stylish sandal left lying on the stairs.

*

The air in Enugu smelled of rain and fresh grass and hope and new anthills. I watched as market traders and grandmothers and little boys hugged Nnamdi, caressed his Army uniform. Justifiable heroism, Obi called it. Obi was thirteen, my bespectacled brother who read a book a day and went to the Advanced School For Gifted Children and was researching the African origin of Greek civilization. He didn't just touch Nnamdi's uniform, he wanted to try it on, wanted to know exactly what the guns sounded like. Mama invited Nnamdi over and made him a mango pie. "Your uniform is so *debonair*, darling," she said, and hung around him as though he was her son, as though she had not muttered that I was too young, that his family was not quite *suitable*, when we got engaged a year ago.

Papa suggested Nnamdi and I get married right away, so that Nnamdi could wear his uniform at the wedding and our first son could be named Biafrus. Papa was joking, of course, but perhaps because something had weighed on my chest since Nnamdi entered the army, I imagined having a child now. A child with skin the color of a polished mahogany desk, like Nnamdi's. When I told Nnamdi about this, about the distant longing somewhere inside me, he pricked his thumb, pricked mine, although he was not usually superstitious, and we smeared our blood together. Then we laughed because we were not even sure what the hell that meant exactly.

*

The Igbo say that the maker of the lion does not let the lion eat grass.

*

266

I watched Nnamdi go, watched until the red dust had covered his boot prints, and felt the moistness of pride on my skin, in my eyes. Pride at his smart olive uniform with the image of the sun rising halfway on the sleeve. It was the same symbol, half of a yellow sun, that was tacked onto the garish cotton tie Papa now wore to his new job at the War Research Directorate everyday. Papa ignored all his other ties, the silk ones, the symbol-free ones. And Mama, elegant Mama with the manicured nails, sold some of her London-bought dresses and organized a women's group at St. Paul's that sewed for the soldiers. I joined the group; we sewed singlets and sang Igbo songs. Afterwards, Mama and I walked home (we didn't drive to save petrol) and when Papa came home in the evenings, during those slow months, we would sit in the verandah and eat fresh anara with groundnut paste and listen to Radio Biafra, the kerosene lamp casting amber shadows all around. Radio Biafra brought stories of victories, of Nigerian corpses lining the roads. And from the War Research Directorate, Papa brought stories of our people's genius: we made brake fluid from coconut oil, we created car engines from scrap metal, we refined crude oil in cooking pots, we had perfected a homegrown mine. The blockade would not deter us. Often, we ended those evenings by telling each other, "We have a just cause," as though we did not already know. Necessary Affirmation, Obi called it. It was on one of those evenings that a friend dropped by to say that Nnamdi's battalion had conquered Benin, that Nnamdi was fine. We toasted Nnamdi with palm wine. "To our Future Son-In-Law," Papa said, raising his mug towards me. Papa let Obi drink as much as he wanted. Papa was a Cognac man himself, but he couldn't find Remy Martin even on the black market, because of the blockade. After a few mugs, Papa said, with his upper lip coated in white foam, that he preferred palm wine now, at least

he didn't have to drink it in snifters. And we all laughed
too loudly.

*

*The Igbo say -- the walking ground squirrel sometimes
breaks into a trot, in case the need to run arises*

*

Enugu fell on the kind of day in the middle of the
harmattan when the wind blew hard, carrying dust and
bits of paper and dried leaves, covering hair and clothes
with a fine brown film. Mama and I were cooking
pepper soup -- I cut up the tripe while Mama ground the
peppers -- when we heard the guns. At first I thought it
was thunder, the rumbling thunder that preceded
harmattan storms. It couldn't be the Federal guns
because Radio Biafra said the Federals were far away,
being driven back. But Papa dashed into the kitchen
moments later, his cotton tie skewed. "Get in the car
now!" he said. "Now! Our directorate is evacuating."

We didn't know what to take. Mama took her manicure
kit, her small radio, clothes, the pot of half-cooked
pepper soup wrapped in a dishtowel. I snatched a
packet of crackers. Obi grabbed the books on the
dining table. As we drove away in Papa's Peugeot, Mama
said we would be back soon anyway, our troops would
recover Enugu. So it didn't matter that all her lovely
china was left behind, our radiogram, her new wig
imported from Paris in the case that was such an
unusual lavender color. "My leather-bound books," Obi
added. I was grateful that nobody brought up the
Biafran soldiers we saw dashing past, on the retreat. I
didn't want to imagine Nnamdi like that, running like a
chicken drenched by heavy rain. Papa stopped the car
often to wipe the dust off the windscreen, and he drove
at a crawl, because of the crowds. Women with babies
tied to their backs, pulling at toddlers, carrying pots on
their heads. Men pulling goats and bicycles, carrying

wood boxes and yams. Children, so many children. The dust swirled all around, like a see-through brown blanket. An exodus clothed in dusty hope. It took a while before it struck me that, like these people, we were now refugees.

*

The Igbo say that the place from where one wakes up is his home.

*

Papa's old friend, Akubueze, was a man with a sad smile whose greeting was "God Bless Biafra." He had lost all his children in the massacres. As he showed us the smoke-blackened kitchen and pit latrine and room with the stained walls, I wanted to cry. Not because of the room we would rent from Akubueze, but because of Akubueze. Because of the apology in his eyes. I placed our raffia sleeping mats at the corners of the room, next to our bags and food. But the radio stayed at the center of the room and we walked around it everyday, listened to it, cleaned it. We sang along when the soldiers' Marching Songs were broadcast. *We are Biafrans, fighting for survival, in the name of Jesus, we shall conquer, hip hop, one two.* Sometimes the people in the yard joined us, our new neighbors. Singing meant that we did not have to wonder aloud about our house with the marble staircase and airy verandahs. Singing meant we did not have to acknowledge aloud that Enugu remained fallen and that the War Directorate was no longer paying salaries and what Papa got now was an *allowance.* Papa gave every note, even the white slip with his name and ID number printed in smudgy ink, to Mama. I would look at the money and think how much prettier than Nigerian pounds Biafran pounds were, the elegant writing, the bolder faces. But they could buy so little at the market, those Biafran pounds.

The market was a cluster of dusty, sparse tables. There

were more flies than food, the flies buzzing thickly over the graying pieces of meat, the black-spotted bananas. The flies looked healthier, fresher, than the meat and fruits. I looked over everything, I insisted, as if it was the peacetime market and I still had the leisure that came with choice. In the end, I bought cassava, always, because it was the most filling and economical. Sickly tubers, the ones with grisly pink skin. We had never eaten those before. I told Mama, half-teasing, that they could be poisonous. And Mama laughed and said, "People are eating the peels now, honey. It used to be goat food."

*

The months crawled past and I noted them when my periods came, scant, more mud-colored than red now. I worried about Nnamdi, that he would not find us, that something would happen to him and nobody would know where to find me. I followed the news on Radio Biafra carefully, although Radio Nigeria intercepted so often now. Deliberate jamming, Obi said it was called. Radio Biafra described the thousands of Federal bodies floating on the Niger. Radio Nigeria listed the thousands of dead and defecting Biafran soldiers. I listened to both with equal attention, and afterwards, I created my own truths and inhabited them, believed them.

*

The Igbo say that unless a snake shows its venom, little children will use it for tying firewood.

*

Nnamdi appeared at our door on a dry-aired morning, with a scar above his eye and the skin of his face stretched too thin and his worn trousers barely staying on his waist. Mama dashed out to the market and bought three chicken necks and two wings, and fried

270

them in a little palm oil. "Especially for Nnamdi," she said gaily. Mama, who used to make Coq Au Vin without a cookbook.

I took Nnamdi to the nearby farm that had been harvested too early. All the farms looked that way now, raided at night, raided of corn so tender they had not yet formed kernels and yams so young they were barely the size of my fist. Harvest of desperation, Obi called it. Nnamdi pulled me down to the ground, under an ukpaka tree. I could feel his bones through his skin. He scratched my back, bit my sweaty neck, held my down so hard I felt the sand pierce my skin. And he stayed inside me so long, so tightly, that I felt our hearts were pumping blood at the same rhythm. I wished in a twisted way that the war would never end so that it would always have this quality, this quality of nutmeg, tart and lasting. Afterwards, Nnamdi started to cry. I had never even considered that he could cry. He said the British were giving more arms to Nigeria, Nigeria had Russian planes and Egyptian pilots, the Americans didn't want to help us, we were still blockaded, his battalion was down to two men using one gun, some battalions had resorted to machetes and cutlasses. "Didn't they kill babies for being born Igbo, eh?" he asked.

I pressed my face to his, but he wouldn't stop crying. "Is there a God?" he asked me. "Is there a God?" So I held him close and listened to him cry, and listened to the shrilling of the crickets. He said goodbye two days later, holding me too long. Mama gave him a small bag of boiled rice.

I hoarded that memory, and every other memory of Nnamdi, used each sparingly. I used them most during the air raids, when the screeching ka-ka-ka of the anti-aircraft guns disrupted a hot afternoon and everybody in the yard dashed to the bunker -- the room-sized hole

271

in the ground covered with logs -- and slid into the moist earth underneath. Exhilarating, Obi called it, even though he got scratches and cuts. I would smell the organic scent, like a freshly tilled farm, and watch the children crawl around looking for crickets and earthworms, until the bombing stopped. I would rub the soil between my fingers and savor thoughts of Nnamdi's teeth, tongue, voice.

*

The Igbo say -- let us salute the deaf, for if the heavens don't hear, then the earth will hear

*

So many things became transient, and more valuable. It was not that these things had value, it was that the ephemeral quality hanging over me, over life, gave value to them. And so I savored a plate of cornmeal, which tasted like cloth, because I might have to leave it and run into the bunker, because when I came out a neighbor may have eaten it, or given it to one of the children.

Obi suggested that we teach classes for those children, so many of them running around the yard chasing lizards. "They think bombings are normal," Obi said, shaking his head. He picked a cool spot under the kolanut tree for our classroom. I placed planks across cement blocks for chairs, a wooden sheet against the tree for a blackboard. I taught English, Obi taught Mathematics and History and the children did not whisper and giggle in his class as they did in mine. He seemed to hold them somehow, as he talked and gestured and scrawled on the board with charcoal (later he ran his hands over his sweaty face and left black patterns like a design.) Perhaps it was that he mixed learning and playing -- once he asked the children to role-play the Berlin conference; they became Europeans partitioning Africa, giving hills and rivers to each other although they didn't know where the hills and rivers were. Obi played Bismarck. "My contribution to the young Biafrans, our leaders of tomorrow," he said, glowing with mischief.

I laughed, because he seemed to forget that he, too, was a future Biafran leader. Sometimes even I forgot how young he was. "Do you remember when I used to half-chew your beef and then put it in your mouth so it would be easier for you to chew?" I teased. And Obi made a face and said he did not remember.

The classes were in the morning, before the afternoon sun turned fierce. After the classes, Obi and I joined the local militia -- a mix of young people and married women and injured men -- and went 'combing,' to root out Federal soldiers or Biafran saboteurs hiding in the bush although all we found were dried fruits and groundnuts. We talked about dead Nigerians, we talked about the braveness of the French and Tanzanians in supporting Biafra, the evil of the British. We did not talk about dead Biafrans. We talked about anti-kwash, too, how it really worked, how many children in the early stages of kwashiorkor had been cured. I knew that anti-kwash was absolute nonsense, those leaves were from a tree nobody used to eat, they filled the children's bellies but gave no nourishment, definitely no proteins. But we *needed* to believe stories like that. When you were stripped down to sickly cassava, you used everything else fiercely and selfishly -- especially the ability to choose what to believe and what not to believe.

I enjoyed those stories we told, the lull of our voices. Until one day, we were at an abandoned farm wading through tall grass when we stumbled upon something. A body. I smelled it before I saw it, a smell that gagged me, suffocated me, a smell so bad it made light-headed. "Hei! He's a Nigerian!" a woman said. The flies rose from the bloated body of the Nigerian Soldier as we

273

gathered round. His skin was ashy, his eyes were open, his tribal marks were thick eerie lines running across his swollen face. "I wish we had seen him alive," a young boy said. "*Nkakwu*, ugly rat," somebody else said. A young girl spit at the body. Vultures landed a few feet away. A woman vomited. Nobody suggested burying him. I stood there, dizzy from the smell and the buzzing flies and the heat, and wondered how he had died, what his life had been like. I wondered about his family. A wife, who would be looking outside, her eyes on the road, for news of her husband. Little children who would be told, "Papa will be home soon." A mother who had cried when he left. Brothers and sisters and cousins. I imagined the things he left behind -- clothes, a prayer mat, a wooden cup used to drink kunu.

I started to cry.

Obi held me and looked at me with a calm disgust. "It was people like him who killed Aunty Ifeka," Obi said. "It was people like him who beheaded unborn babies." I brushed Obi away and kept crying.
*
The Igbo say that a fish that does not swallow other fish does not grow fat.
*

There was no news of Nnamdi. When a neighbor heard from their son or husband in the front, I hung around their room for days willing their good fortune to myself. Nnamdi is fine, Obi said in a tone so normal I wanted to believe him. He said it often during those months of boiled cassava, months of moldy yams, months when we shared our dreams of vegetable oil and fish and salt.

I hid what little food we had because of the neighbors, wrapped in a mat and stuck behind the door. The neighbors hid their own food too. In the evenings, we all unwrapped our food and clustered in the kitchen, cooking and talking about salt. There was salt in Nigeria, salt was the reason our people were crossing the border to the other side, salt was the reason a woman down the road was said to have run out of her kitchen and tore her clothes off and rolled in the dirt, wailing. I sat on the kitchen floor and listened to the chatter and tried to remember what salt tasted like. It seemed surreal now, that we had a crystal saltshaker back home. That I had even wasted salt, rinsing away the clumpy bottom before re-filling the shaker. Fresh salt. I interspersed thoughts of Nnamdi with thoughts of salty food.

And when Akubueze told us that our old pastor, Father Damian, was working in a refugee camp in Amandugba, two towns away, I thought about salt. Akubueze was not sure, stories drifted around about so many people being at so many places. Still, I suggested to Mama that we go and see Father Damian. Mama said yes, we would go to see if he was well, it had been two long years since we saw him. I humored her and said it had been long -- as though we still paid social calls. We did not say anything about the food that Caritas Internationalis sent to priests by secret night flights, the food that the priests gave away, the corned beef and glucose and dried milk. And salt.

*

Father Damian was thinner, with hollows and shadows on his face. But he looked healthy next to the children in the refugee camp. Stick-thin children whose bones stuck out, so unnaturally, so sharply. Children with rust-colored hair and stomachs like balloons. Children whose eyes were swallowed deep in their faces. Father Damian introduced Mama and me to the other priests, Irish missionaries of the Holy Ghost, white men with sun-reddened skin and smiles so brave I wanted to tug at their faces and see if they were real. Father Damian

275

talked a lot about his work, about the dying children, but Mama kept changing the subject. It was so unlike her, something she would call *unmannered* if somebody else did it. Father Damian finally stopped talking about the children, about kwashiorkor, and he looked almost disappointed as he watched us leave, Mama holding the bag of salt and corned beef and fish powder he gave us.

Why was Father Damian telling us about those children? Mama shouted as we walked home. What can we do for them? I calmed her down, told her he probably just needed to talk to someone about his work and did she remember how he used to sing those silly, off-tune songs at church bazaars to make the children laugh?

But Mama kept shouting. And I too began shouting, the words tumbling out of my mouth. Why the hell did Father Damian tell us about those dying children, anyway? Did we need to know? Didn't we have enough to deal with?

*

Shouting. A man walked up the street, beating a metal gong, asking us to pray for the good white people who were flying food in for the relief center, the new one they set up in St. Johns. Not all white people were killers, gong, gong, gong, not all were arming the Nigerians, gong, gong, gong.

At the relief center, I fought hard, kicking through the crowds, risking the flogging militia. I lied, cajoled, begged. I spoke British-accented English, to show how educated I was, to distinguish me from the common villagers, and afterwards I felt tears building up, as though I only had to blink and they would flow down. But I didn't blink as I walked home, I kept my eyes roundly open, my hands tightly wrapped around whatever food I got. When I got food. Dried egg yolk.

276

Dried milk. Dried Fish. Cornmeal.

The shell-shocked soldiers in filthy shirts roamed
around the relief center, muttering gibberish, children
running away from them. They followed me, first
begging, then trying to snatch my food. I shoved at
them and cursed them and spit in their direction. Once I
shoved so hard one of the men fell down, and I didn't
turn to see if he got up all right. I didn't want to
imagine, either, that they had once been proud Biafran
soldiers like Nnamdi.

*

Perhaps it was the food from the relief center that made
Obi sick, or all the other things we ate, the things we
brushed blue mold from, or picked ants out of. He
threw up, and when he was emptied, he still retched
and clutched at his belly. Mama brought in an old
bucket for him, helped him use it, took it out
afterwards. I'm a chamber pot man, Obi joked. He still
taught his classes but he talked less about Biafra and
more about the past, like did I remember how Mama
used to give herself facials with a paste of honey and
milk? And did I remember the soursop tree in our
backyard, how the yellow bees formed columns on it?
Mama went to Albatross hospital and dropped the
names of all the famous doctors she had known in
Enugu, so that the doctor would see her before the
hundreds of women thronging the corridors. It worked,
and he gave her diarrhea tablets. He could spare only
five and told her to break each in two so they would last
long enough to control Obi's diarrhea. Mama said she
doubted that the 'doctor' had even reached his fourth
year in medical school, but this was Biafra two years
into the war and medical students had to play doctor
because the real doctors were cutting off arms and legs
to keep people alive. Then Mama said that part of the
roof of Albatross hospital had been blown off during an

air raid. I didn't know what was funny about that but Obi laughed, and Mama joined in, and finally I did, too.

*

Obi was still sick, still in bed, when Ihuoma came running into our room, a woman whose daughter was lying in the yard inhaling a foul concoction of spices and urine that somebody said cured asthma. "The soldiers are coming," Ihuoma said. She was a simple woman, a market trader, the kind of woman who would have nothing in common with Mama before Biafra. But now, she and Mama plaited each other's hair every week. "Hurry," she said. "Bring Obi to the outer room, he can hide in the ceiling!" It took me a moment to understand, although Mama was already helping Obi up, rushing him out of the room. We had heard that the Biafran soldiers were conscripting young men, children really, and taking them to the front, that it had happened in the yard down our street a week ago, although Obi said he doubted they had really taken a twelve-year-old. We heard too that the mother of the boy was from Abakaliki, where people cut their hair when their children died, and after she watched them take her son, she took a razor and shaved all her hair off.

The soldiers came shortly after Obi and two other boys climbed into a hole in the ceiling, a hole that appeared when the wood gave way after a bombing. Four soldiers with bony bodies and tired eyes. I asked if they knew Nnamdi, if they'd heard of him, even though I knew they hadn't. The soldiers looked inside the latrine, asked Mama if she was sure she was not hiding anybody, because that would make her a saboteur and saboteurs were worse than Nigerians. Mama smiled at them, then used her old voice, the voice of when she hosted three-course dinners for Papa's friends, and offered them some water before they left. Afterwards,

278

Obi said he would enlist when he felt better. He owed it to Biafra and besides, fifteen-year-olds had fought in the Persian war. Before Mama left the room, she walked up to Obi and slapped his face so hard that I saw the immediate slender welts on his cheek.

The Igbo say that the chicken frowns at the cooking pot, and yet ignores the knife.
*

Mama and I were close to the bunker when we heard the anti-aircraft guns. "Good timing," Mama joked, and although I tried, I could not smile. My lips were too sore, the harmattan winds had dried them to a bloody crisp during our walk to the relief center and besides, we had not been lucky, we got no food.

Inside the bunker, people were shouting Lord, Jesus, God Almighty, Jehovah. A woman was crumpled next to me, holding her toddler in her arms. The bunker was dim, but I could see the crusty ringworm marks all over the toddler's body. Mama was looking around. "Where is Obi?" She asked, clutching my arm. "What is wrong with that boy, didn't he hear the guns?" Mama got up, saying she had to find Obi, saying the bombing was far away. But it wasn't, it was really close, loud, and I tried to hold Mama, to keep her still, but I was weak from the walk and hunger and Mama pushed past me and climbed out.

The explosion that followed shook something inside my ear loose, and I felt that if I bent my head sideways, something hard-soft like cartilage would fall out. I heard things breaking and falling above, cement walls and glass louvers and trees. I closed my eyes and thought of Nnamdi's voice, just his voice, until the bombing stopped and I scrambled out of the bunker. The bodies strewn across the street, some painfully close to the bunker entrance, were still quivering, writhing. They reminded me of the chickens our steward used to kill in Enugu, how they flapped around in the dust after their throats had been slit, over and over, before finally laying quiet. Dignity dance, Obi called it.

I was bawling as I stared at the bodies, all people I knew, trying to identify Mama and Obi. But they were not there. They were in the yard, Mama helping wash the wounded, Obi writing in the dust with his finger. Mama did not scold Obi for being so careless, and I did not rebuke Mama for dashing out like that either. I went into the kitchen to soak some dried cassava for dinner.
*

Obi died that night. Or maybe he died in the morning. I don't know. I simply know that when Papa tugged at him in the morning and then when Mama threw herself on him, he did not stir. I went over and shook him, shook him, shook him. He was cold.

"*Nwa m anwugo*," Papa said, as though he had to say it aloud to believe it. Mama brought out her manicure kit and started to clip Obi's nails. "What are you doing?" Papa asked. He was crying. Not the kind of manly crying that is silence accompanied by tears. He was wailing, sobbing. I watched him, he seemed to swell before my eyes, the room was unsteady. Something was on my chest, something heavy like a jerry can full of water. I started to roll on the floor, to ease the weight. Outside, I heard shouting. Or was it inside? Was it Papa? Was it Papa saying nwa m anwugo, nwa m anwugo. Obi was dead. I grasped around, frantic, trying to remember Obi, to remember the concrete things about him. And I could not. My baby brother who made wisecracks and yet I could not remember any of them. I could not even remember anything he said the night before. I had felt that I had Obi for a long, long time and that I did not

280

need to notice him, really notice him. He was there, I felt, he would always be there. I never had the fear that I had about Nnamdi, with Obi, the fear that I may mourn someday. And so I did not know how to mourn Obi, if I could mourn Obi. My hair was itching and I started to tear at it, felt the warm blood on my scalp, I tore some more and then more. With my hair littered on our floor, I wrapped my arms around myself and watched as Mama calmly filed Obi's nails.

*

There was something feverish about the days after Obi's death, something malarial, something so numbingly fast that it left me free to not feel. Even Obi's burial in the backyard was fast, although Papa spent hours fashioning a cross from old wood. After the neighbors and Father Damian and the crying children dispersed, Mama called the cross shabby and kicked it, broke it, flung the wood away.

Papa stopped going to the War Research Directorate and dropped his patriotic tie into the pit latrine, and day after day, week after week, we sat in front of our room -- Papa, Mama and me -- staring at the yard. The morning a woman from down the street dashed into our yard, I did not look up, until I heard her shouting. She was waving a green branch. Such a brilliant, wet-looking green. I wondered where she got that, the plants and trees around were scorched by January's harmattan sun, blown bare by the dusty winds. The earth was sallow.

The war is lost, Papa said. He didn't need to say it though, we already knew. We knew when Obi died. The neighbors were packing in a hurry, to go into the smaller villages because we had heard the Federal soldiers were coming with truckloads of whips. We got up to pack. It struck me how little we had, as we packed, and how we had stopped noticing how little we had.

*

The Igbo say that when a man falls, it is his god who has pushed him down.

*

Nnamdi clutched my hand too tight at our wedding. He did everything with extra effort now, as if he was compensating for his amputated left arm, as if he was shielding his shame. Papa took photos, telling me to smile wider, telling Nnamdi not to slouch. But Papa slouched, himself, he had slouched since the war ended, since the bank gave him fifty Nigerian pounds for all the money he had in Biafra. And he had lost his house -- our house with the marble staircase -- because it was declared abandoned property and now a civil servant lived there, a woman who had threatened Mama with a fierce dog when Mama defied Papa and went to see her beloved house. All she wanted was our china and our radiogram, she told the woman. But the woman whistled for the dog.

"Wait," Mama said to Papa, and came over to fix my hat. She had made my wedding dress and sewn sequins unto a secondhand hat. After the wedding, we had pastries in a café and as we ate, Papa told me about the wedding cake he used to dream about for me, a pink multi-layered cake, so tall it would shield my face and Nnamdi's face and the cake-cutting photo would capture only the groomsman's face, only Obi's face.

I envied Papa, that he could talk about Obi like that. It was the year Obi would have turned seventeen, the year Nigeria changed from driving on the left hand side of the road to the right. We were Nigerians again.

282

§ § §

*Chimamanda Ngozi Adichie was born in Nigeria in 1977
and grew up in the university town of Nsukka. She
studied communication and political science in
Connecticut, graduating summa cum laude.*

*Her short fiction has been published or is forthcoming
in The Iowa Review, In Posse Review, Prism
International, Calyx Journal, Wasafiri, Other Voices and
the anthology 'Proverbs For The People.'*

*She was short-listed for the Caine Prize for African
Writing 2002 and was a runner-up in the
Commonwealth Short Story Award 2002.*

*Her first novel, Purple Hibiscus, will be published by
Algonquin Books of Chapel Hill in the Fall of 2003.*

DECEMBER 2002

SHORT STORIES

FOLLOWING THE STAR

by Jim Boring

> *We returned to our places, these Kingdoms,*
> *But no longer at ease here, in the old dispensation,*
> *With an alien people clutching their gods.*
> *I should be glad of another death.*
>
> *(from "Journey of the Magi, " T.S. Eliot)*

Well, Misha, I think it is time to tell you the story of how we followed the star. The ache in my chest tells me that it may be now or never. Come sit beside me. Bring me that wine flask. No, no, don't make faces at me, the wine can't hurt me now - it helps ease the pain. Sit. Sit.

It begins in Damascus We had convened the first formal meeting of what were then known as Magi. There were Stoics and Epicureans and Cynics and Skeptics from Greece, and camp followers from Rome; there were sorcerers from Cilicia, astrologers from Syria, conjurers from Egypt. It was wonderful. We talked about physics and philosophy and magic and entertained each other with tales of manipulating rulers and common men alike.

It was during these discussions that I first met Balthazar and Melchior. Balthazar was the blackest man I have ever seen. He was an Ethiopian, tall and regal looking, a man of the desert but also very much a man of the world. His robes were as black as his skin and trimmed in gold. He wore an emerald the size of a shekel in his turban, which was also black and gold. An impressive man at first sight and even more impressive once fully known. As black as Balthazar was, that was how white Melchior was. He had no pigmentation to his skin at all.

His eyes were pink and his hair was as white as his skin. Melchior was a man of the night. The stars were more familiar to him than the sun. Outside during the day he wore gloves of the finest silk from his home in Babylon and his strange eyes peered intently from the slit of the white turban he kept wrapped securely around his face. At night, however, Melchior would unwrap himself in great relief. He would unwind his turban and wear it like a long scarf over his robes. The gloves would be put away and his hands and face would almost glow in the moonlight.

What brought the three of us together was the natural bond of a common interest -- the stars. Balthazar practiced a form of astronomy unknown to either Melchior or me. It took us a while to become oriented to the differences in our various symbols and classifications. We spent many a late night spinning tales of astral discoveries and laughing together at the absurdities of some of our former beliefs. Thank god for the wandering Greeks, if we hadn't the language they strewed about so indiscriminately in their travels, we would never have been able to talk to each other.

Melchior was the most accomplished of us. He seemed to live in the stars. During the day he would assiduously write down his most minute observations from the night before. He had a double tent, a tent within a tent that screened the sun sufficiently for him to work in comfort.

The ostensible reason we studied the stars was to better understand the will and the ways of God. The real reason was because we found the stars themselves so interesting. If there was a God behind them that was fine with us, if not, the stars justified themselves. Misha, my fawn, please don't turn away. I have lived long enough to know that whoever God is, He has a very high tolerance for foolishness on the part of his creatures. If He can put up with Caligula, I feel pretty safe from his wrath. Come, little one, sit next to me again.

Where was I? Ah, the wine flask. At any rate, the three of us became friends--talking and studying and drinking and arguing together. Very enjoyable. Our natures were to be solitary men -- alone with the stars and our speculations. So it was a rare privilege for us to find kindred spirits. When the gathering of the Magi concluded and, one by one, the other magi and their followers went their separate ways, we lingered on, unwilling to put our conversation to an end. Our retinues attended us and muttered among themselves about the increasing time away from their families.

At last all the others, save one, had left us. This man seemed to stay behind more of weariness than interest in us or our discussions. He was a Semite, worn and old, dressed in tattered rags and the goatskin favored by ascetics. His name, we had learned, was Antiochus and his science was not one of observation or study but rather one of offering himself as an object of study to his God. He was a stylite, a man who lived alone in the desert, sitting endlessly on a pillar, naked to the sun and the wind. As we laughed and drank and argued, he sat as a kind of silent rebuke to us. This was not someone you would invite to enliven a party. No, no, Misha, I mean no disrespect. I am in awe of the degrees to which man will go to seek what truth there is in the world. Who am I to mock their methods? All I meant was that our innocent gambols seemed like the orgies of Gomorrah next to this man. He never spoke to us, but he did speak. He spoke, we thought, to God. It was hard to tell. He mumbled and the language he spoke was a form of Hebrew dialect that none of us recognized. He kept his face upturned and his long beard blew about his ravaged face in the wind. He was a sight to see, a terrible, somehow inspiring sight.

291

Balthazar had among his entourage a man who cared for and trained birds and animals that through chance or deliberate capture had come into his keeping. Trained creatures like these, Misha, are always a good way of breaking the resistance of audiences -- royalty and common folk alike. When they see a wolf lie down with a lamb, they tend to listen more closely to the one who has made the seeming miracle. In this man's keeping was a crow that had been trained to bring bits of food to Balthazar -- to fly to him, perch on his shoulder and place the particles directly into Balthazar's mouth. Now the crow was taught to bring food to the stylite. It would swoop down on Antiochus straight out of the sun, land on one of the man's skeletal legs and drop food into the clay bowl that nestled against his shriveled scrotum. Misha! Please, sit down. All right, I won't say scrotum. I'm sorry. The old man never moved, never stopped his mumbling to God, never even seemed to notice the bird, even when it pecked at him to get his attention. Very strange. But much stranger things were yet to come.

It was the fourth or fifth night of our lingering conversation. We had allowed our fire to go out and we lay in a row together, our heads pillowed in our bundled turbans, Melchior glowing between Balthazar and me. It was the night of the new moon and the stars lit up the sky in what seemed to us to be the playful exuberance of children loosed from the domination of their austere mother, the moon. We could hear Antiochus murmuring in the dark, we could hear the wind rustling the palms around the rancid oasis, and we could hear the frogs in that pungent water, calling to each other.

Balthazar told us that his people had an interesting belief about frogs. He said that in Ethiopia the frog was honored as a cleansing spirit, that its song brought the rain that washed the earth and that the rain not only

292

cleaned the earth and drove down the dust but that it also washed away the sins of the people. Good for the frogs, I said. Good for the people, Melchior added. And then we were silent as we thought about the story and watched the stars.

After a while Melchior spoke. Without preamble he said, we have a similar legend. Ours concerns dragonflies, which we believe have the power to transform illusion into reality and reality into illusion. Both Balthazar and I expressed our approbation of this wonderful belief. Illusion into reality and reality into illusion we exulted. The perfect emblem of the magi, Balthazar said. Iridescent, elusive, faster than the eye can follow, I said, we should officially adopt the image. Our vote was unanimous and we took Antiochus's mumbling for assent. That is why you see the dragonfly woven into my robes, Misha. Had I told you about the dragonfly? Oh. Ah, well. Please, the flask. Thank you. It was late, the pauses in our conversation lengthened; only Antiochus murmured endlessly on. And then suddenly we were fully awake. Antiochus began a strange keening sound that rose and fell in a kind of -- how can I describe it -- a kind of strangely joyful song. This weird music coming from that ravaged, hairy instrument was accompaniment to the most amazing sight any of us had every seen. Our fingers pointed simultaneously toward the heavens.

A star had appeared in the eastern sky -- a new star. Oh, Misha, how can I describe our excitement? It was beautiful, a distinct white globe from which long, lovely spikes of illumination extended. It was a jewel and also unmistakably a herald, a sign of things to come. We laughed, we wept, we danced to the tune of old Antiochus. We knelt and prayed, with sincerity we prayed to our various gods and to the universe itself. We prayed in thanks and in fear and we prayed for wisdom in interpreting this singular event. None of us had ever seen such a thing before. Yet, surely, we would be the authority to which people would turn to explain the phenomenon. What would we say? When we had exhausted ourselves we sank down again into our orderly little row and thought a long while in silence. The song of Antiochus went on unabated, it seemed now to somehow accompany the song of the frogs, there was a harmonic quality to their music, they seemed to be aware of each other and to be synchronizing their individual vocalizations into a larger chorale.

Imagine us, Misha, there in the deep desert night -- a man of such blackness he merges with the dark; a man so white he glows; a man almost not a man, body and soul scoured and scourged by sand and a desperate seeking after God, a blazing new star that dwarfs anything else in the sky -- and me, small and trembling in a mixture of fear and anticipation. Oh, it was a night, Misha. It was a night.

Balthazar noticed first. It is moving, he said. We watched a while. It was moving we agreed. But not with the rest of the sky, Melchior said. We watched again awhile. It goes its own way, I said, very strange. We watched the whole night. When the sun broke the horizon all the stars fled but the new arrival. Even in daylight it shone brightly enough that the sun could not blot it from the sky. We wondered at that and what it implied about the quality of the blue dome of the daylight sky. Was the star behind the blue and shining through it? Was it beneath the blue? What was going on?

Antiochus was gone -- nowhere to be seen. In our preoccupation he must have shouldered his squat pillar and disappeared into the desert. Melchior withstood the sun as long as possible and then reluctantly took to his tent. We joined him there.

You know what we must do, I said to the others. They nodded in agreement. We have to, Melchior said, it is our duty. It seems to be heading southwest toward the land of the Hebrews, Balthazar observed. But, he added, does it have a destination or only a direction? What do the prophecies say about a star? Anything? Melchior seemed to remember something about a prophecy concerning the birth of a Hebrew messiah being announced by a new star, but couldn't remember the origin of the prophecy. I was no help, my own opinion of ancient prophecies being that since anything of significance could be traced back to a prophecy, they weren't of much value.

Misha, please! Don't get so upset -- everything isn't sacrilege. If you don't learn to think for yourself you're of no more value to God than your parakeet is to you -- just an amusing pet. We are here to help God find the truth, Misha, not merely to accept the truth someone else has found. Each of us must add our small finding to the whole, and the whole is still a long way off. This is a noble task, Misha -- and you cannot avoid it by a slavish obedience to the law or to custom -- you have to do the work yourself. Now, give me the flask again and sit down, there is more.

We began to follow the star. Not knowing how long this journey might take we each sent most of our entourage home on short rations and added theirs to our supplies. We traveled mostly at night to accommodate Melchior's tender skin, although if we thought we were falling behind the star we would try to get a couple of early morning hours before Melchior had to take to his tent.

On the first night we came on Antiochus. We could hear him singing before we saw him, legs crossed, arms raised, sitting on his ridiculous pillar with the wind blowing his dirty hair and goatskin vest and the sand encrusted on his face and beard. Each morning he was

gone and each evening we came upon him. He had no
camel, no food supplies; he might as well have been
naked to the sun and the wind -- I don't know how but
each day he covered as much distance as we did. We
continued the practice of sending Antiochus food
through the services of the crow. The smell of the man
and his potential as a carrier of some leprous desert
disease made us keep him at a distance. One day the
crow refused to leave Antiochus. Balthazar tried
everything to get him to return but the bird only cawed
and strutted about the stylite's pillar and walked across
his legs and perched on his head. He had clearly chosen
a new master. I remember telling Balthazar he had lost
a bird. But he shook his head and said that the bird
knows where it belongs.

We marked the days and nights of our journey and the
position of the star on our sky charts. There was no
retrograde motion to the star; it kept to its course as if
steered by a heavenly hand. To see such a wonder even
once in a life is a rare privilege. We felt it so. Our
nightly rides were mostly silent except for the snorting
and shuffling of the camels. We each fell into the
rhythmic, rolling motion of the animals and dwelt in our
own individual reveries regarding the star. During the
day we discussed our thoughts and compared our
speculations. Just us, three men who knew how little we
knew, despite our reputations, talking together. There
was no hypocrisy in Melchior's double tent where we
gathered each morning and in which we had all taken to
sleeping together. We were engaged in direct exposure
to a mysterious and wonderful event. It may have good
or terrible consequences. Our plan, such as it was, was
not to explain it yet but only to observe it and catalog
its actions and its characteristics. The simplicity and the
beauty of our role in relation to the star humbled us all.
It made us feel like true scientists. We owed nothing to
our patrons or to the public -- we were a band of
brothers on a noble quest for whatever truth we might

puzzle out together from this gift of the gods. One
morning Balthazar said he had been thinking about the
dragonfly legend. Odd, said Melchior, last night I was
thinking of your frogs. Why did these stories come to
our attention on this occasion, Balthazar asked. Do they
have something to do with the star? When did the
stories come to us, I asked. On the night the star
appeared, just before we saw the star we shared those
stories, Melchior answered. A coincidence probably, I
said. Or a key to understanding the star, he replied. The
star and the stories appeared together, Balthazar
mused. Together. We lapsed into our usual silence as
we thought about the possibilities in this pairing.

Illusion and reality, Melchior began in the kind of
condensed manner we often used to spark a train of
thought. Cleansing and purification, I said to extend the
thought. To cleanse is to clarify, Balthazar said and
added, and to clarify is to cut through illusion to reality.
Another silence ensued. We took our separate thoughts
into our separate sleep. The silence continued through
the night as we traced our narrow track on the earth
beneath the moving star.

This thing is what it is, I thought, yet it is also what we
make it. We project our purposes and our hopes onto it.
Is that illusion? It is if it obscures the reality of the star.
Is it metaphor? It is if it clarifies an aspect of our own
purpose. But is even a clarifying metaphor an illusion?
What do you think, Misha? No, no, don't tell me what
you have read. What do you think? Ah, that's all right,
child -- it will come, it will come. And it comes the way
it did that night -- slowly as you talk to yourself, as you
question yourself, as you test your integrity against
questions posed by the stars, as you ask yourself to be
truthful, to not pretend, to be what man was meant to
be -- the explainer and the appreciator of all things. We
are both dragonfly and frog. In one role we clean the
lens of our mind's eye and look on the world without

the filtering influence of opinion or custom or law. In the other we recognize the illusory quality of the things we see, how reality often hides itself in mystery, how mystery seduces our intellect into the search for truth and how clarity and illusion and truth form a bond of enticement and reward that keeps both our heart and our mind engaged in the quest. Ha, too much, I see. You want the story of the star and I give you lectures. Forgive me, Misha. My flask.

After over a month following the star, Misha, my little orthodox treasure, it had become as familiar to me as the shaggy, undulating behind of Balthazar's camel. The trek we undertook in awe and wonder had taken on some aspects of a duty. Not that we were discouraged or contemplating breaking off our great quest -- still, not to put too fine a point on it, we were bored. Eventually even the extraordinary lapses into ordinary. So it was as our journey passed its second fortnight.

A wind from the southwest, the direction we were traveling, had been blowing for six days. The wind made conversation difficult, it kept our heads down into our turbans and our bodies hunched over our saddle horns as we rode. We struggled to keep the star in sight through the blowing sand and the racing clouds. Even during the day the wind seemed to sap our strength and our will to talk. A quiet, almost morose pall seemed to have settled on us. The wind was relentless and each night when we would come upon Antiochus and the crow, the sand would have mounded up around the pillar and in Antiochus's lap and the crow would be huddled out of the wind, nestled behind Antiochus. With the wind in our faces we could hear the stylite's strange song well before we could see him in the blowing sand. On the seventh night the wind simply stopped. It did not abate gradually it just stopped. The moon came out full and luminous. The star shone in all its glory and we followed it easily. An hour later

Melchior said, It has stopped. Yes, I said in agreement, and not a moment too soon, it was beginning to blow the marrow from my bones. Not the wind, Melchior said, the star.

We halted our camels. We watched for nearly an hour. It had stopped. Beyond a dune we could hear Antiochus singing. Where are we, I asked. Near a town called Bethlehem as far as I can tell, said Melchior. I suggested we cross the dune and camp near Antiochus and we did. The old man and the crow were as we always found them, Antiochus arranging himself in a lotus position on his pillar, his arms laid loosely across his legs, his palms upward, his interminable song droning on and on -- even in his sleep. The crow flapping about on the gaunt shoulders of his master, seeming to dust him at day's end -- then squatting and settling down for the remainder of the night.

We watched awhile, speculating on the meaning of the halt in the star's progression, then, too tired to think or talk more we retired to Melchior's tent and fell quickly asleep. It must have been near midnight when the crow started cawing. All of us half-woke and grumbled about it. What's got into the crow, Balthazar asked, it has never done anything like that before. Then, as though the sun had risen suddenly to its midday height, the tent was flooded with light. The three of us thrashed about in our bedclothes trying to disentangle ourselves and get to our feet. We rushed out of the tent into a sight even more amazing than the star itself.

The sky was filled with light and the source of the light was a host of winged figures, half bird, but with bodies of men and women that crowded the night sky. And they were singing beautiful music, the most beautiful sound I have ever heard. They were everywhere, above us high in the sky, around us hovering over the ground. We could make out the features and forms of those closest to us. Naked, their skin glowed every color imaginable. The men's muscles varied in size as much as their colors did. The women were tall and willowy or short and thick, their breasts hung low on their bellies or pointed upward like pastry tops. They were very human but in every way as unlike humans as you can imagine. But one and all they were beautiful beyond anything I have ever seen before or since. And, wonder of magical wonders, there, soaring among them, were Antiochus and the crow. But what an Antiochus, no longer the ravaged madman of the desert but a glowing, glorious vision of perfection. And he was laughing, a full, happy chortle. He beckoned us to him.

Our analytical, scientific natures fell away. In the face of a miracle, Misha, just trust your instincts. We did. Then and there we stripped off our robes and opened our raised arms to the experience. Like leaves lifted by the wind we rose into the heavenly host, soared, laughed and sang with Antiochus and the angels. That is what these creatures were, Misha -- angels. Nothing in our legends or my poor imagination leads to any other conclusion. These angels cavorted in the sky like drunken guests at a wedding dance. As rare and beautiful as they were, they themselves seemed transformed into an even more exalted condition by the event they were celebrating.

For it was true, Misha, a messiah had been born that night in Bethlehem. I know it to be true. For the four of us and the crow soared among the angels with a purpose we only sensed, a purpose that led us to a point high above a shepherd's manger. It was there the star had stopped and now stood flaring a beam of light down into the humble shack where a naked newborn child suckled at its mother's breast and shepherds crowded round and knelt before the child. We stood there in the night sky and saw all this, Misha. We heard the alleluia sung in a mighty chorus and saw the angels weave their voices and their colors in a tapestry of sound and sight that I cannot adequately describe to you. And there was a scent that night, Misha, something delicate, a sort of toasted cinnamon smell -- something that simply lingered in the air like the perfume of heaven. Sometimes it comes back to me. We could see the child. There was nothing godlike about him. He suckled contentedly, his eyes squeezed closed as if to avoid the celestial light, one tiny hand resting near his mother's nipple. Just a child.

And then we rose again as if a volcanic explosion had sent us reeling up and backward from the manger spewing us and music and light high into the sky. Antiochus gently somersaulted, head over heels and his once croaking voice now sang clear and full in a distinct patrician Latin baritone. He sang, "Gloria, gloria, in excelsus Deo," over and over again in wonderful musical variation.

And then we were in our tents asleep. When we woke it was dawn. We looked at each other as though we each had a guilty secret to hide. We didn't know what to say to each other. You could see it in our faces. We were like children who having been left alone by their mother get into some innocent mischief, which they cannot explain. We each dressed quickly and went outside one at a time. The star was gone. It was true, Melchior said. Balthazar and I nodded in agreement. They were here, weren't they? Melchior asked. Yes, we said, they were here and we saw what we saw and did what we did. I don't know what to say, Melchior said. Nor did we. Antiochus was also gone. We don't know where he went but we jokingly speculated that he was probably somersaulting his way across heaven with his angelic friends. We hoped so anyway.

Well, that's the story, Misha. You know the rest of it. How we found Herod and asked for his help in finding the child again. How that madman murdered every child in the area under two years old in order to avoid any possibility of having his miserable throne usurped. How I came back here to Mecca and have spent my life waiting for the messiah to make himself known. Now I am an old man dying. I had hoped that the millennium had arrived and that I would see its fulfillment. But there has been nothing. If the messiah was born that night, Herod must have killed him. Thirty years have gone by and there has not been another sign. Misha, give me the wine flask again; there may be some dregs.

§ § §

Jim Boring lives on the Illinois-Wisconsin border from which vantage point he is able to peer into the woods dark and deep or the city equally dark and deep. He has published in the small press and in the Chicago Tribune Magazine.

He is a Contributing Editor and Marketing Director of Literary Potpourri

PUPA

by Julia Ravenscroft

Your tree's dead easy to climb, even for a girl. Keith was right; it was. The branches of our mulberry tree stretched invitingly to the ground, sturdy arms to gather you up, set you shoulder-high and let you see the whole world.

I'd scramble up and ease my way through leaves the size of my father's hand. All around me dangled the mulberries - glossy, swollen leech-berries. I'd pick one, squeeze it between finger and thumb and watch the magenta juice trickle down my wrist. Beneath bruised fruit flesh a pale hard core.

It's such a shame to waste all those mulberries, but they're only good for jam. My mother always meant to make jam, but she never did. Each summer the tight pale berries swelled through shades of red until they were bloated, almost black and oozing juice. By the time I went back to school they were plopping softly to the ground, bloodying the earth at the foot of the tree.

The cocoon spun by the caterpillar of the moth Bombyx mori is made of silk, Claire. Do you know the only thing silkworms eat? Mulberry leaves. My father told me all sorts of wonders. When I asked him what cottonworms ate, he just laughed. It didn't matter because I didn't want to catch any cottonworms - all my dresses were made of cotton anyway. My mother had a silk dress. I loved to run my fingertips over the skirt, so smooth and cool. Surely there had to be silkworms in our tree. I thought I could catch some, keep them like I'd kept the grasshopper, in a shoebox, but this time I'd punch air holes in the lid. If I fed them the most tender mulberry leaves I could find, they would spin for me. Spin and spin an endless silken thread, from which I would weave a dress as diaphanous as a dragonfly's wing. I'd straddle the scaly branches, examining the underside of leaves for silkworms, but I never found any, only wasps, floating drunkenly on the fermented air.

For goodness' sake, Claire, you're giving me a headache. How can I concentrate on my crossword with you running about? Go outside and play. My mother banished me from the house most days, grumbling under her breath that the summer vacation was ridiculously long. Exiled to the garden, I'd cocoon myself in the tree where I'd sit swinging my legs and listening for the boys.

That day sounds of Indians on the warpath drifted over the garden wall. I parted the leaves, the silkworms' salad, and squinted into the piercing sunlight. In the distance the braves, Mark and Keith, were whooping and scalping and dancing the rain dance along the lane to the woods.

And I don't want you playing in the woods with those little ruffians. It's time you started acting like a young lady. My mother would send me to play with soppy Sarah and her dolls, but I'd sneak away because boys were much more exciting than Barbies.

I shuffled along the branch that overhung the wall and dropped to the ground. But the braves had already gone haring off in pursuit of cowboys, hapless settlers or a rival tribe.

In the woods there are zombies and monsters and ghosts waiting to jump out and get you. I didn't really believe Keith, at least not any more, but it was still a bit

304

scary in the woods, unless you were with the boys of course; they weren't afraid of anything. That afternoon, the only things lying wait for me were brambles that whipped out to snag my dress.

Rat-a-tat-tat! Machinegun fire. I'd been ambushed.

Mark's tousled blond head appeared from behind a laurel bush.

- Can I play, Mark?

- All right, but you'll have to be the Japs. Keith and me are the commandos.

Dodging bullets and mortars, I stumbled shrieking over the shattered bodies of my comrades littering the battlefield and leapt, mortally wounded, into my trench. Naturally inferior in firepower and bravery, I was doomed from the start. Pursued by Colonel Keith and Captain Mark, brothers in arms, I was slaughtered unmercifully only to be reincarnated as an ally for the next challenge.

Girls can't climb the wall, only easy things like Claire's tree. I had to remain at base camp, said Keith; only boys were allowed to climb Mount Everest. I was secretly glad, not relishing the scraped knees and cut hands, the danger inherent in being a boy. Shouting encouragement I sat cross-legged on the grass. Mark, lithe and athletic, reached the summit first and perched gingerly on the spiky, flint-topped peak, his feet dangling over the precipice. Keith, knees scabbed and bloodied, not content to sit, stood erect with arms outstretched and shouted to Simon riding his bike down the track on the other side of the Himalayas. When Mark and Keith grew weary of the rarified atmosphere they made the perilous descent back to base camp for our next adventure.

A ferocious dragon, the fires of Hell burning in his belly, lurked in the forest, waiting for maidens to devour. This was my favorite of all Keith's games. Gorgeous in my bejeweled silks, dreaming maidenly dreams of princes, I cantered through the forbidden forest on my chestnut horse. The dragon, aroused by the sweet scent of maiden's blood, swooped down in a burst of steam and grabbed me in its razor claws. In a flap of scaly wings I was whisked off to his misty mountaintop lair. Sir Keith the Courageous and Sir Mark the Mighty valiantly charged into the fetid cave, crunching underfoot the charred bones of less fortunate maidens. Brandishing their broadswords, they casually minced up the maiden-eating monster. But without even asking for my hand in marriage, Sir Mark the Mighty said:

- We're going, Claire. See you.

- Can I come too?

A shrug in reply from Mark, from Keith a scowl.

- No. No girls. Come on, Mark.

- Why not?

- 'Cause we're going to be blood brothers.

They ran off into the woods, imitating the beat of war drums, Indian braves once more. I was wounded, really this time and I felt my cheeks flush hot. I didn't understand. Before I'd been tolerated if not welcomed. The boys were always in need of someone to play an enemy or a maiden in distress.

I crept after the flashes of color, Keith's red t-shirt and Mark's blue, as the boys plunged through the fecund growth of summer. Sticky-sharp grasses lashed my bare legs and nettles stung my sandaled feet, but I didn't care. I knew where the boys were going: the circle of five trees.

At the edge of the clearing where we had often played together, I stopped, crouched behind a bush and watched, feeling the resentment of the uninitiated.

Keith pulled a penknife from his pocket, unsheathed the blade and calmly etched a fine red line across his wrist. Mark, pale-faced, no longer a brave, stared at the outstretched hand offering the ritual knife. He hesitated. Keith laughed, pushed the knife towards him. Mark shook his head. Keith began to march around him, chanting. No words, only rhythm. He broke into a run, now whooping and yelling, tracing ever-tighter circles until, only inches from Mark, he stopped. The woods still echoed with his shouts as the boys faced each other. Mark took the knife and, without a word, nicked his wrist. Keith clamped it to his own bloodied wrist with a piece of string he took from his pocket. Thus bound, brothers forever, their blood mingling, they hurtled madly around the circle.

At the fifth tree they saw me.

- What's she doing here? Spying on us, I bet.

- Leave her alone, Keith. Come on, Let's go.

- No. She has to do it too. The spy's scared, aren't you, Claire?

I shook my head.

He cut the string binding him to Mark, grabbed my wrist and pulled me into the circle.

- Here. I dare you.

He handed me the knife, its blade edge tinged with red.

- I'll do it if I can be Mark's blood brother.

- Sure, I don't care.

I pressed the blade to my wrist. I dared not look at the blood, my blood, so I shut my eyes. It didn't hurt much. I held out my hand for Mark, but felt no cool skin press mine, no potent boy's blood pulse through my veins. There was only laughter. I opened my eyes. Keith's mocking face was right against mine. He pointed to my wrist. No blood, just a faint, girly-pink impression.

- God, girls are so stupid! Here, I'll do it for you.

He caught my hand and held the knife against a slender turquoise vein.

- No!

I jerked my arm away and backed up. Keith and Mark just stood there, staring. I wondered what was wrong with them.

On the heel of my hand a shiny red bead was forming where the knifepoint had punctured my skin. It was wonderful. I raised my arm; at last an equal, an initiate.

- You said you would, Mark. You said we'd be blood brothers.

Mark didn't move. Something like fear glimmered in his eyes. I did not understand. Boys were never afraid of anything.

- What's the matter, Mark? You did say...Make him, Keith.

But Keith, the fearless adventurer, now looked anything but. Amazingly he began to back away - from me.

- God, that's freaky! Mark, come on. Don't touch her.

- You promised I could be a blood brother too if I did it, and look, blood, my blood. I took a step towards Keith. He turned and shot out of the circle, crashing through the undergrowth to the path.

Mark remained, as I knew he would. I offered him my hand. Slowly he extended his arm, but before we could touch he pulled back and sprinted after Keith.

- Wait! I don't want to play this game. We haven't finished the blood brother one yet. Come back!

But they didn't and I was alone amongst the silver trees. No sound but the hum of insects. My blood-bead, never to be threaded with Mark's, was hardening. As I stood there a laser-focused sunray penetrated the leafy membrane above. I looked down, blinking sunspots from my eyes. The mossy ground was aglow with an unbearably intense neon-lit green such as I had never seen before. The radiance lasted a mere moment before its potency was expended and I saw what the boys had seen: between my feet crimson drops soaking into the spongy earth.

§ § §

Julia Ravenscroft spends far too much time writing and seriously neglects her husband, teenage sons and two cats. She has just finished her first novel, a light-hearted mystery set in her native Great Britain. This is her first published story.

INSIDE 553

by Michael Davidson

The fifth floor Men's bathroom is closed today. Locked for no one to use. There is no sign posted on its door warding off the public, nothing at all that makes it seem even slightly different on the outside than any other bathroom in the Regenstein Library, just the plain gray door with a black plaque mounted on the center indicating the room number: 553 MEN.

I don't know how I feel about this.

When I was still alive this bathroom was open for use. The only prerequisite for entry was your sex. You had to be male, and that I was. Every now and then I would take a hiatus from my duties as a student and 553 would serve as my respite. Sometimes I would do the more obvious things in here, like urinate in the urinal, or defecate in the toilet, or wash my hands in the sink. Other times I would do things not quite as obvious but still expected from all normal men, like masturbate, or stare at myself for prolonged periods in the mirror checking for blackheads and making sure my hair was sufficiently disheveled.

That was about all I used to do inside 553 during my freshman and sophomore year as an undergraduate. And then I got myself a girlfriend, my first girlfriend.

Up until then I had gotten to the point where I masturbated at least three times a week inside 553, and to tell you the truth, I was beginning to feel a bit ashamed of myself. I was a twenty-year-old virgin masturbating in a public bathroom three times a week. Sure, there were other guys out there that were similar to me in this perverse respect, but I didn't know any of them and that made me feel just that much lonelier. The only thing I had going for me was that I didn't masturbate anywhere else. So, my room and bathroom were free from all innuendoes of the sinful act. However, the reason why I limited masturbation to inside 553 was not out of self-discipline. I lived in a dorm with other people, and to get caught masturbating amongst the only people I saw and conversed with on a regular basis would've been an irrevocable blow to my delicate ego. Therefore, I only did it inside the single stall of 553, which, over time, had grown to be more like my home away from home.

Anyhow, my first and last girlfriend was Julie. I met Julie in one of my classes and, unlike every other occasion when I was attracted to a girl, I somehow mustered up the audacity to ask her out on a date. I thought it would be nice if we went to see a Friday night movie together at the theater on campus. She agreed.

When Friday night came I thought it would be best if I looked as though I was completely indifferent towards the whole event. I left my hair messy as it had been all day, I didn't change into decent looking clothes, and I made sure I looked overly exhausted. She, on the other hand, looked great when I saw her that night with her straight red hair and an outfit that was conservative and alluring. Her lips were shaped perfectly without lipstick, her eyes could've been blue, green, or purple, depending on the light around her, and her ears made me want to take her into my arms and kiss them until she could hear my longing. I felt like masturbating.

During the entire duration of the movie I was thinking exclusively about what to do after the life on the screen died and there was nothing left to watch. I asked myself: Should I take her to a coffee shop and talk? Should I ask if she wants to come back to my place and talk there? Or should we just walk around campus until we got bored? Don't ask me why, but I went in favor of the latter.

After the movie ended we walked aimlessly around campus until it was unanimously decided that things should stop before we killed ourselves; the whole night was filled with this dreadful silence that only worsened when one of us opened our mouths:

"Did you like the movie?" I asked her.

"Yeah."

A minute of silence.

"What did you like about it?" she asked me.

"I never said I liked it."

Another minute of silence.

"Oh. I got the impression that you liked it," she said contritely.

"Not really."

I ended up taking her home shortly thereafter and saying goodnight with a distant hug, no kiss. She was cute, and I liked her way of being, but we weren't great at being social people, or at least I wasn't.

The next time we had class together I avoided her as best I could by sitting in the back and not saying a word. Of course, I could've refrained from going to class all together, but something inside me wouldn't let that happen; maybe it was hope. Sure enough, when the professor let class out, Julie clumsily found her way to the back of the classroom and tapped me on the shoulder even though I was already looking at her.

"Want to do something this Friday, I mean, if you're free?"

I couldn't believe she was asking me out after our previous nightmare together. Was she that desperate? I looked down at the carpeted floor, which was what I usually did when I wanted to give off that faraway, languid feeling, and then looked up at her wondering if she would be hurt if I said no. It's not that I wanted to say no to her, it's just that I didn't know if I could be subjected to the horror of another gauche evening.

"Sure," I said. I had far too much to lose if I told her otherwise. I was a twenty-year-old virgin who masturbated regularly inside 553.

"Okay. Let's meet on the first floor of the Reg then at, say, seven o'clock."

I said sure again. She said bye and left promptly.

That Friday I went to eat dinner at Pierce Dining Hall before my second date with Julie. This time I was a little more relaxed since she asked me out and seemed as though she had a plan that wouldn't leave us in a perpetual state of awkwardness.

I walked back to my dorm room after a semi-satisfying meal and thought about what to wear. In the past I had gone with the indifferent look because if things didn't work out, at least I didn't get stuck appearing as though I actually cared. In other words, my look was designed in anticipation of my failure. However, the indifferent look didn't quite work to my advantage last time with Julie so I figured it would be unadvisable to go for that look again. This time I would try to look presentable. I decided to wear my only pair of khakis, a white long-sleeved dress shirt, which I would tuck in, and a black belt with black shoes. When I studied myself in the mirror I was taken aback: never in my life had I looked so good and so vulnerable; I kept my hair uncombed to give me a way to deal with possible failure.

When I got to the Reg she was already waiting with a messenger bag strapped diagonally around her torso, from right shoulder to left hip. Once again, she had dressed well for the occasion, wearing a pair of fitted blue jeans and a baby-blue shirt one size to small with a neckline that exposed the horizontal beauty of her collarbone. And once again I felt like masturbating. She waved and I couldn't believe she was waving at me.

"There you are," she said. "You look nice. Really."

"What did you want to do at the Reg?"

Everything about me was rude and abrupt.

"Well, I thought it would be fun to go back in the stacks and watch some short films on my laptop."

"What?"

"You know, there're Ethernet connections in the stacks . . ."

"So?"

I didn't realize I had interrupted her until it already happened.

"Well, it's really easy to watch short films because the connections are so fast. I usually go back there when I study so that I can watch films whenever I get bored."

I still was not quite sure what she was talking about but decided to just follow her lead anyway, which was unusual for me . . .

You see, I'm really an uptight guy even though I try not to act like it; I hate when people are late and I never like wasting more time than necessary, that's why I don't go out much. There are too many things to do during the day for me to hang out. Most people would never know this about me. They only know the person that talks extensively about getting plastered and sleeping a lot and spending an obscene amount of time on the couch watching television, but none of that is true. I'm a serious guy. I study all the time. I care about my future. You might be wondering why I went out on this date then. Honestly, I don't know. Every now and then I would think about how much work I could be getting done if I were on the fifth floor studying in the stacks instead of spending time with Julie, but something inside of me repudiated that thought before it had a chance to take another breath.

"Do you have a preferred floor?" she asked me when we got inside the elevator.

"Actually, I do."

I pressed the button leading to the fifth floor, it glowed, and we started on our way up to the top.

"You like the fifth floor?" she asked.

"Yeah."

"I usually work on the third floor."

"Third floor is too busy for me."

"C'mon, it's not that bad."

She smiled and I could feel the ice pick breaking into

the ice.

The elevator door opened, and we walked into the stacks. The stacks was an intimidating place for most people. It was an enormously quiet area with countless shelves of books and nothing else except for good size desks running along the circumference. If you wanted to get a lot of work done, you would plant yourself in one of these desks and work without interruption; the desks looked straight at a wall so there was little possibility of distraction. I loved working on these desks. In fact, I couldn't work anyplace else on the fifth floor.

I led her to the desk where I usually worked in the stacks hoping that there was no one already there. There wasn't, so we sat down. She got her laptop up and running as I waited petulantly in the chair.

"All right, let's see here . . . ," she said curiously.

Julie was searching the Internet for different sights with short films. I can't remember any of the names, but there were a lot of them.

"Here we are. This is my favorite sight. It has no censorship, which gives it plenty of variety."

It was a colorful sight with a long list of short films. She clicked on one of the blue titles and a small black screen immediately popped up. There was a buffering period, which lasted a few seconds, and then the movie began. It was called "Ridiculous Me." Julie laughed out loud at nearly every corner of the dialogue. I did too. The film was actually very humorous. It consisted of a series of incompetent mistakes and at the end of each mistake different people from off the street would be filmed saying, "ridiculous me," without knowing what preceded their comment.

The next film was just as entertaining, but it was more of a drama. It was called, "Illumination." I appreciate drama more than anything else. It seems to me that everyday life is teeming with such diverse emotions and in order to do it any justice there must be passionate love affairs, painful cries of separation, mounds of symbolic imagery, carefully constructed metaphors, and tragic death. Without these ingredients, any medium of creative art is doomed for failure. "Illumination" was a success.

"That was great." I said after the film ended without being asked. "I really enjoyed that."

"You did?"

"Yeah, it had the drama of life in every scene."

"I didn't know you liked dramas?"

"I love dramas! How else could there be love? How else could there be pain?"

Julie stayed quiet and looked at me like never before. A book fell onto the linoleum floor behind us. She gave a startled jump, placed her hand on her heart, and smiled unknowingly. I had a feeling that now would be the perfect time to unite lips, but I didn't have the courage to go through with it. Instead, the word osculate echoed in my head and a waterfall of inane thoughts submerged me.

"Let's watch one more," I said with a gasp.

"Okay."

She ran down the list and found one called "The Fury of Love." The opening scene showed a man's fists hitting a demure woman in the face. The woman's face split open more with every landed blow, but she never retaliated, she never even cried in pain. After a sixty-second bout the woman's face was no longer demure. It was a bloody pulp. Then the camera rotated around so that it shifted from seeing the man's fists to seeing the profile of the man's entire body. As the camera zoomed out it became apparent that there was no woman to begin with, the man was looking into a shattered mirror painted in his own blood. He knelt down on the ground and cried with the palms of his hands covering his entire face as his blood left him.

The remainder of the film was nothing but pornography; fifteen minutes of hardcore love scenes between the same man in the beginning and the same demure woman who ended up not really being there in the end. Sexual sounds shattered the silence of the stacks as beautiful breasts bobbed up and down in different positions of penetration. The film concluded with a long embrace between the two lovers.

"Wow! Now that was intense," said Julie.

"Y-Yeah."

I could barely speak. I was far too preoccupied with trying to conceal my erection underneath my khakis.

"I n-need to g-go to the bathroom. I'll be r-right back. Okay?"

I stood up quickly and left with my hands over my crotch. It was refreshing to see 553 waiting for me close by. I walked in, went straight to the single stall, unzipped my khakis, and started masturbating with religious fervor. Julie would be wondering what I was doing in the bathroom, especially after watching "The Fury of Love," if I took any longer than a few minutes. I had to speed things up. Fast stroke - faster stroke - fastest stroke, the tip of my penis was beginning to enlarge, when . . .

. . . there was a knock on the door. I stopped momentarily to make sure that my senses were not deceiving me. The knock came again, slightly louder than before. I didn't know what to do. 553 might've been my home away from home, but the only prerequisite for entry was your sex; other men were free to use 553 without permission from inside.

"It's open," I said with a dry, cracked voice.

The door creaked ajar.

"Hi," a voice said in a whisper. "It's Julie."

What! I screamed on the inside.

Julie was on the cusp of entering 553. But she didn't meet the prerequisite; she was a female God damn it. I panicked. I looked down at my right hand wrapped around my penis and felt like dying on the spot. Here I was inside 553 masturbating, and my date was ten feet away from me.

"Uh . . . uh, I'll be out in a minute, Julie. Wait just a sec. Wait."

"Okay."

I heard the gray door close. I was safe from being discovered in the most pathetic of all human conditions. I looked down again at my penis and noticed it was hanging flaccidly. What a fucking relief. I was saved. I thought about finishing what I was doing before the unexpected interruption, but on second thought I decided against that understanding that the risk was far too great. I flushed the toilet quickly to make it seem like I was doing something normal in there and exited the stall in such a rush that I forgot to zip up my khakis.

Julie was standing right in front of me with her upper four teeth pressing down on her plump bottom lip. I thought she had left. My face went pale. My heart shuddered. I didn't know what to do. When I opened my mouth and tried to speak, she put her finger over my lips and shook her head in disagreement. I stayed quiet with my zipper down.

"I know what you were doing in there," she said.

How could she have known? The stall wasn't transparent. Or was it? Of course it wasn't transparent.

I replied in an almost plaintive voice, "Y-Yeah. I w-was going to the bathroom, Julie. That's all. What did you th-think I was doing?"

Cold sweat. Cold sweat coming from my armpits.

"Oh no you weren't. Don't lie. You were doing this."

She slipped her right hand passed my fallen zipper and got hold of my penis through my briefs. I couldn't believe what was happening. Her hand started stroking, not missing a beat, and I grew hard again.

"Weren't you?" she asked with a tinge of sultriness leaking from the sides of her mouth.

I didn't know how to answer her question. Was it even a question? If I said yes, she would think I was pathetic and probably stop doing what she was doing . . . but I liked what she was doing. If I said no, she would probably stop on the spot out of embarrassment . . .

but damn, I liked what she was doing. You see my dilemma? On another note, I couldn't help but wonder how experienced Julie was at this. I was feeling mighty good with her warm hand stroking my penis, much better than if I was doing it alone in the stall of 553, but was this the same Julie that watched short films in the stacks? Maybe I misunderstood her from the very beginning.

"Touch my breasts," she said peremptorily.

"O-okay."

I won't go into further detail for the sake of unnecessary gratuitousness. Suffice it to say that we ended up having sex inside the stall. The same stall that had seen me masturbate an inordinate amount of times saw me pleasure a member of the opposite sex; saw me lose my virginity. It must've been proud of me, like parents watching their only son walk, though clumsily, for the first time.

In this way, at the beginning of my junior year, 553 miraculously transformed into the pad of a sexually active guy. And things were hot for quite some time . . .

At least three times a week, after several hours of studying, Julie and I would meet inside 553 to have sex just like that first time, except slightly more suave, at least I'd like to think that. Don't think that other males didn't come into the bathroom while the two of us were going at it; we had plenty of visitors, but it was all right since, like I've said before, the stall wasn't transparent. After our cavorting in the bathroom stall, we both came out refreshed and ready to start studying some more. In this way, I was a substitute for her short films, and she was a substitute for my masturbation. It was a convenient setup.

However, it would be foolish and misleading of me to give you the impression that our relationship only came to life inside 553. On the contrary, we often took walks around campus after class, ate together at Pierce Dining Hall, talked on the phone before we went to sleep, and so on. There were even times when we left the campus entirely and went to eat dinner downtown. Granted, these sojourns outside of Hyde Park didn't have too great a frequency, but they did happen nevertheless.

After a couple months of frolicking with Julie in more than one way, I realized that I was participating in that often celebrated relationship between man and woman; that unspoken bond between two individuals that can be so sweet, so sweet it becomes sour. Julie was my girlfriend, and I was her boyfriend.

I even started calling her Jules.

Jules this and Jules that.

"I love you, Jules."

"I love you, too."

Time passed in this pristine fashion. O! what a joyous time it was. I was smiling without knowing it. I was sleeping in such an ineluctable calm. I was dancing among the puffy white clouds on the lightest feet in the world. I was the man.

But eventually the escapades inside 553 started declining in frequency: from three times a week to two times a week to one time a week to no times a week. You had to have seen this coming.

You did, but I didn't. I didn't.

To the best of my knowledge she never started seeing

another guy or anything like that. We didn't even get into one of those catastrophic arguments that end up destroying everything and nothing between two people caught up in proclamations of love and raging hormones. It was just an unexpected farewell on her part that happened after class. Everyone had left except for the two of us. I was still seated, writing down some last minute notes. She was hovering over me with a palpable droopiness that, at the time, I considered rather becoming. I should've known better.

"I think we should start seeing less of each other," she said without making eye contact.

I stopped writing.

"But why, Jules? Did I do something wrong?"

"It's complicated."

The pen fell from my limp fingertips.

"What're you saying? That it's over?"

"I know it hurts, but you have to trust me. It's for the best."

I felt the strings attaching my heart to the rest of my body snapping. I looked into her eyes - they were green at the time - to search for some uncertainty, maybe even fear of a future without me in her life. I waited for a small hint of a smile and some words claiming that she took everything back, that she still loved me. But nothing except unwavering conviction bled from her pores.

"But I thought you loved me?" I desperately asked.

"That's the thing. I don't think I ever did."

"Are you serious? How can you say that?"

"I just don't think I ever did. We had lots of sex. And I enjoyed it. I guess I confused things."

"Confused things? Jesus Jules. I loved you. I love you. What should I think now?" I said this with a thick snake in my throat.

"Don't think anything. Just get over it. We had a fling that I confused for love. But now I know it wasn't love. I'm young. I can't love anyone right now. Don't take it personally."

"You really mean it, don't you, Jules? You're breaking up with me."

"Yes."

She promptly left the room.

My heart dropped so long and so hard that it created the eye of a maelstrom that would eventually be my demise. I was alone again, but this time without my heart.

You have to understand. Jules was my first love. I was not capable of understanding what life would be like after my first love. Not only was I not capable, I was afraid. Afraid to live life alone again after having grown so terribly used to the comfort of that other hand.

During the following nights, while sleeping alone with opened eyes in my dorm room, I would feel sour tears roll down the contours of my pallid cheeks. Without blinking, more sour tears would well up, slide into the openness, and cake my face in a melancholic gleam. My nose sniffed desperately for an opening, but only found layers of mucous. It got so bad that I felt as though I could no longer breathe. But why should I breathe in the first place now that Jules was gone?

During the following days, to at least try and get over our breakup, I spent all my time studying on the fifth floor. Obsessing over class work. That is, until I died in the struggle. Death claimed me on the day that everything exploded in front of my sallow face . . .

But even now, when no one can see, hear, feel, taste, or smell me, I still study on the fifth floor of the Reg back in the stacks, but I changed desks because it's impossible for me to walk passed my usual desk without conjuring up images from that first night of watching short films with Jules, even though I'm already dead - imagine that. Everything about that night is colorful and vivid, almost as if it's more alive than the actual night. I even remember the alarming expression on her face when she commented on "The Fury of Love."

"Wow! That was intense."

That's what she said with big, owl eyes as she raised her left arm and used those ceramic fingers of hers to comb back several strands of red hair behind her left ear, which was shaped like a wonderful question mark.

Now I study directly opposite that desk, on the east end of the stacks instead of the west end, and never dare make the mistake of moving in an easterly direction again. I already made that mistake one time shortly after her schismatic words, and what followed was, unlike our relationship, indelible. It went something like this . . .

Once I sat down at that desk, everything about Jules flowed into me with an unrelenting force that resulted

325

in me heaving in and out with suffocating breathes and miserable tears. I felt like a gong being smacked one time, two times, three times until the smacking eventually stopped and all that remained was the vibration that slowly attenuated into silence. Random images clambered about inside of me: a stone being hurtled into the ocean, a dog eating a cat, the sun burning all nine planets, a mountain transforming into a ripe breast and then disappearing into a disappointing mist, a finch talking with Darwin and explaining what really happened, a pair of fists repeatedly hitting a deceiving mirror.

I knew I had to do something, and the only thing I could do was follow the commands from inside me. I went to look for Jules on the third floor. It was not like I expected to mend our severed relationship, I did not even expect to find her, but I had to at least try. When I reached the third floor stacks everything looked the same as on the fifth floor, except I knew that the books were of a different subject matter. I walked around the periphery hoping that she would be studying, or maybe watching another short film if she was bored with the studying. She was not doing either. I told myself she was not there and decided to go back to the fifth floor and study. However, when I was making my way back to the stairwell I happened to pass the women's bathroom. The door was the same gray as my 553, but the black plaque read: 351 WOMEN. I would've just walked right by had I not heard moaning sounds coming from inside. There was no question about who it was. She was saying those two words that seem to stretch on forever under certain circumstances.

"Yea yeeeeessssss!"

I thought about opening the door, but I didn't meet the only prerequisite; I wasn't female. So I stood outside and listened carefully. There came those two words again. They were killing me.

She was with another guy and I loathed her for it. Even if I were canonized a saint I would still loathe her for doing what she was doing inside that bathroom. Heck, I would probably punish her with divine fury and then fix the halo above my pious head.

My thoughts raged on and on in this manner as those two words stretched inside the bathroom. I felt like trampling through the gray door and yelling something so profane everything would come to a halt and the tryst would end with her and her new lover shrinking so small that I would proceed to stomp them mush mush mush with both my gigantic feet.

However, in spite of my irate disposition, I felt my penis starting to throb from those stretched words coming out of her mouth again and again and again. I was aroused.

Notwithstanding my contempt, I imagined kissing her body, groping her body, having sex with her body, and a tingle surged inside me. I had to fight this feeling somehow. It was against my will, God damn it! She was controlling me, controlling how I felt, without even giving me the sex that I had grown so used to; she was giving it to someone else now.

I had to counteract everything she stood for. So I extracted all the personality from her, dehumanized her very being, and transformed her into strictly a body that was made for me to fuck long and hard with zero consideration. I imagined beating her body down with bludgeoning fists as I raped her.

But raping Jules only made me want her body more. Even though it was bruised in variegated blossoms of purple and blue, I still wanted to have sex with her behind the gray door. I thought about going in there and joining them without asking permission. Just insert my penis somewhere and go at it just like that. But I couldn't do it.

Instead, I found myself walking quickly upstairs, with my hand over my crotch, to my home away from home: 553. When the gray door closed behind me - no one else was in the bathroom - I heard a voice that told me: Go into the stall. I entered the stall. There she was: the porcelain toilet with its seat down and a silver-metal plume ascending behind it ready for the flush, waiting for me to ejaculate all over it. Unzip your pants. I used one hand to unzip my pants. The intricate sound of unraveling teeth made my groin shudder. Let your pants drop. My other hand unbuttoned my pants, and they quickly slid down to the tiled floor. This time a cold shiver bolted its way through my hairy bare legs and I could feel the throbbing intensify as my penis elevated to a personal record length in tiny increments. Now do what you know how to do best. I clutched my penis and started masturbating, but with each tingle came a flash image of her body.

I saw her naked breasts sprout hard nipples from her pink aureole as I held them between my groping hands harder than she could handle. She screamed. I saw her panties grow moist in preparation for my entrance: she knew what was going to happen was going to happen, and she wanted to end it quickly without fighting back. I heard her scream again as I stabbed at her clitoris with the point of my tongue and looked up from down below to see all her body coil and release in fear. The screaming grew louder. Books began to fall flat on the linoleum floor outside in the stacks with a wayward bang. The toilet flushed again and again. Men entered and left with bewildered expressions painted on their faces. And then I came all over the toilet seat. Everything left me as my prostate quivered, ripping through her body. She was used and dead in my head. I was satisfied.

I exited the stall of 553 and looked at the mirror expecting to see me, the victor. But no. Never. Staring at me with an untouched gaze was Jules. She was still alive and stunning as ever with red hair everywhere. Her eyes were blue.

"You," I said in disgust. "I thought I killed you."

I did not wait for a response. The drama consumed me. I ran over to the mirror and started cursing and slapping and punching until everything was over. Until I was over.

But no one knows what went on that day inside 553. No one knows about the epic struggle that was played out until its sweet end.

Why isn't there a sign on that gray door, or better yet, a different plaque entirely explaining to the public that there is no such thing as love even if there is such a thing as Jules, and then my name at the bottom to give credit? That's all it would've had to say. "553 MEN It'll kill you."

§ § §

Michael Davidson spends his time writing and reading in Miami, Florida.

This is his first published story.

FLASH FICTION

REPLACEMENT PARTS

by Gail Louise Chagall

The nurse calls. My husband has moved up the heart transplant list. I call my friend Tom to tell him. His cell phone is crackling with static.

"Are you on fire?" I say.

"No," Tom laughs, as if that would be amusing. "I'm just driving to Indiana. Finally got my starter replaced."

I tell him about the transplant list, our number coming up. "It'll probably skid in on a motorcycle," I say. "You know what they call them, right? *Donor* cycles."

He laughs again, that gravelly laugh I'd do anything for, in any position.

"And you know what they call helmets?" he says. "Brain buckets."

Tom remembers his friend Pete doing heroin, riding a Harley with his little brother in back. The brother wore their single helmet and Pete sped clean off Highway 101. At the funeral they said, "Too bad Pete wasn't wearing a helmet. He could have had an open casket."

We catch up. Tom's wife visited his summer retreat, a visit which scotched *our* possible visit. Most of our visits fall through. Then she left and he dreamed the nightmares he has at each departure: execution by hanging, by firing squad, beheading.

"That's original," I say. I'm thinking I couldn't replace her.

"I'm so glad for your husband," Tom says."He's got a date with destiny." Tom is unselfconscious, quite sincere. We are kindly about our spouses on each other's behalf. We are not good marriage material, the two of us. We admire their persistence.

"A date with a loving heart," I say. "Probably barreling down a highway right now."

"Pumped full of heroin and speed," he says.

"What will you do in Indiana?" I ask. We are serious now. More serious. I am glad he's in a car, not on fire, not on *his* Harley. I don't want Tom's organ. Not *that* organ. There are trades you can't make with replacement parts, not with hearts, and not with men.

§ § §

Gail Louise Chagall directs a public interest group in Chicago, IL, USA and is writing for an MFA at the Bennington Writing Seminars.

Her work has appeared in Zoetrope All-Story Extra, FictionFix, The Salt River Review ("Sparta to Elroy" and "The Telemarketer's Point of View") and Brevity, and is upcoming in 3am Magazine and Outsider Ink.

CHERRY ON TOP

by **Katherine Grosjean**

There are loads of kids tonight. We're in my yard, damp evening grass cool on our bare feet, mosquitoes just starting to nibble.

Tonight the games are fast and furious and the neighborhood boys are calling the shots. We've about gone through them all. The Jimmo brothers swept us in Red Rover and are now commandeering Freeze Tag. Someone finally barks "Pile On", and we all inwardly quicken, waiting for a volunteer to take that first dive onto the grass. It's usually Gary Mullen, the big hulking seventh grader who really should be a niner. He likes to lie on his belly, never even takes off his black horn-rimmed glasses, and he eggs on any kid within view; "Come on, ya fruit. Come on! Jump on the pile. Wimp like you? I'd never even feel ya." All the kids back up as far as the hedges allow, and one by one they let out a primal shriek, and run full tilt toward the prone Gary. With a leap into faith they land, hoping their sixty pounds will somehow transform into ninety, and shut him up for good. But Gary just shakes his head and taunts "Come on, Feeb, we can't wait here all night. Pile on, why don't ya?" And his donkey laugh trickles a heehaw through the pile until the whole hill shakes with laughter. He stays like that, with the weight of the neighborhood on his back, for what seems like hours. And he never even blinks.

So here we are, running in tight little adrenaline circles, waiting for Gary to take the dive. I trot slowly, knowing that I'll be the last on. The cherry on top. Sometimes I have to climb bodies to get to the top of the pile; there are that many kids. And I am that small. Tonight is one of those nights.

I'm barely noticed in the moving mayhem. Until I trip on the garden hose, that is. I go down with a thwack, face first, and before I can lift my face from the grass, I hear one of the Jimmos shriek "Pile On", and he lands full length on my back. The wind goes out of me with a low whoosh. To the rest of the gang, it looks like he has taken the dive. Holy cow, Jimmo is down! One by one, they back up to the hedge, release the obligatory war cry, and fling themselves onto the pile. Onto me. The other Jimmo brothers, the Mullens, the Dawsons, all the neighborhood hunks. And their kid brothers and sisters too. It is quite a game.

grass in my mouth, my nose, my eyes. can't turn my head. can't move at all. every part of my body is clamped tight to the earth. fingers, arms, legs, toes, all pinned. pressure builds in jerks from above and below. I can't breathe. god, I can't breathe! I try to yell, squeal, cry through sealed mouth, clogged nose, but only air escapes. my lungs in a vice, I can't replace the air. precious air. sounds are muted, compressed, pillowed. are they laughing? is that the ripple I feel? how many left? I see green, in swirls. is it grass? no, my eyes are closed. I feel heavy so heavy. am I the earth? I taste something, dark and salty. blood. it seeps into my mouth, making me retch in vain. only my tongue and heart in motion. my heart pounds in fury. they must feel it, they must hear it. everything's fading. laughter, voices, heartbeat. someone's turning down the volume. green swirls slow and stop.

Even now, years later, I still sometimes squirm in vain under that hill of flesh.

When pregnant, I used to visualize my baby floating in her dark and pulsing world, sounds muted. I'd picture her cramped, suffocating, unable to see, squeal or cry. I had to stop imagining her.

Caves, crowds, bearhugs, sleeping bags. Now impossible, all.

Sometimes sex gets almost unbearable. Racing heart, senses heightened and distorted, out of control. All quite delicious. Until the weight of him intrudes, until breath becomes jagged, until pressure builds from above and below and within.

I must be on top. The cherry on the cake. Always.

§ § §

Katherine Grosjean lives and writes in rural Ontario, Canada. Her work has appeared or is forthcoming in mélange and Snow Monkey. She hangs out at <u>Painted Moon Review</u> where she is an Assistant Fiction Editor.

DOG AT THE PARK

by Mary McCluskey

I'm watching a girl in a white raincoat throw a ball. Her terrier runs, leaps, skids to catch it, then bounds back, the ball between his grinning teeth, to lay it at her feet. A gift. She laughs and throws again.

Your new woman wears a white raincoat. I hope she throws hard and fast, makes you leap high to catch the ball between aching jaws, and when you lay it at her feet, I hope she laughs.

§ § §

Mary McCluskey is a British journalist who alternates between Los Angeles, California and a small Shropshire village in the UK.

Her work has appeared in a number of publications, including Zoestrope's ALL STORY EXTRA, LINNAEAN STREET, The PAMAUNOK REVIEW, EXQUISITE CORPSE, SALON and ATLANTIC UNBOUND.

She has just completed a novel White Nights, and is working on another.

She is a Contributing Editor of LITERARY POTPOURRI

PHOTO ESSAY

WoodWatching

by Richard Peers

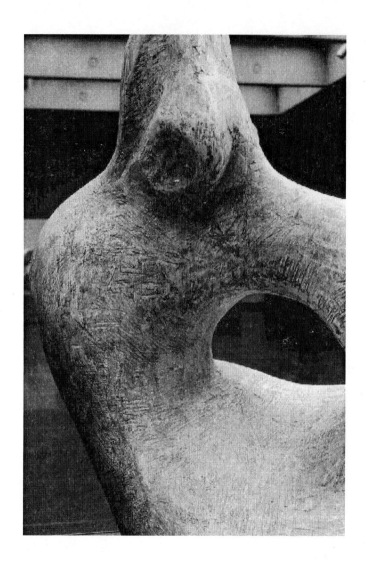

Richard Peers received his diploma in Fine Arts in 1996 from Fanshawe College --Ontario, Canada. He focused primarily on video, photography and mixed media.

The work of Cindy Sherman and Edvard Munch played a major role in the development of Richard's style.

Today Richard lives in Canada and is married to wife Juli and has a son Aidan. Richard continues to grow with his art and owns his own printing company.

POETRY

Oakland

by L.A. Seidensticker

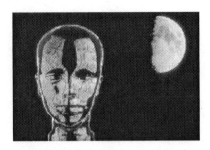

late at night the moon half lit, me
all the way, on a dirt road in the wilderness
through the canyon, nine hundred feet straight down one side
wrack and rock straight up the other, sometimes
the recollected light of Oakland looms up behind me
the headlamps go dusky on the road ahead

and i'm in the hand of god
who knows my sins and doesn't mind them
who spreads Oakland out around me
prowling helicopters, corner bodegas, the old korean
behind the counter
blue jazz, the white bones of eucalyptus

jerry brown
down
in a spotlight
urging up lettuce, arugula,
yoruba

the whispers of the accidental dead
and their grave tenderness
come to claim me on this road
this california moonlit orange blossom buckeye
path into stars

lanterns shining upwards from the bay, the lost
the oasis-eyed san pablo avenue wanderers
i thank you for keeping me close
leap into the pale high cloister of your
Oakland arms
carry me home

§ § §

L.A.. Seidensticker lives in the northern California wine country, very fortunately, two miles of bad road from the pavement.

too many

by Carrie Berry

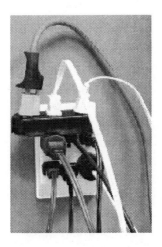

there are too many people in this head
friends that weren't
lovers that didn't
faint others that can't be defined
but won't be confined
to their cabins

the passenger list is too long to sort out
can't bother with making the effort to shout
"bugger off now or cough up the fare"

there are too many people in his head
the skeleton

dancers provide him
no answers while truth begets lies;
a jumble of flies
in the ointment

in judgment he sits but it's so clear to me
there's no chance of his ever getting off free
while he oversees the tribunal

there are too many people in this bed
old bodies, young bodies
undiscerned somebodies
piled high and deep
coming between us
precluding sleep

§ § §

*Carrie Berry left a long time electronics manufacturing
career in the US to pursue a life conducive to her first
love, writing.*

*Living in Scotland for the past five years she has
completed her first novel and is working on two others.
Poetry and short stories fill the time between editing
her two literary web sites:*

fandango virtual
and (with her husband, Jim Maddocks) Bonfire.

IF CASKETS SPOKE

by Janet I. Buck

I go back to your grave
once in a leprous while.
Lay slumping tulips on the stone.
Stalks and cups stare back at me
as if they know the weep, the arch,
the guessing game.
Language is a broken shovel
spooning up the gypsies
of a sweet unknown.
I examine fulcrums of dust
in headstone cracks
like verbs my hands must conjugate.
If caskets spoke full sentences,

would you implore my hammers
on the grieving pail
to cease their tin can rattling,
live in the green of the yellowing grass,
forget these firm unchangeables.

Our photographs are all unframed
in boxes under sagging beds.
All what if's ignite, grow still.
I bring you back my meager way;
fingers and their slivered reeds
know no music, have no beat.
If graves are so inanimate
why do all their stomachs growl --
appear to pairs of passing feet
like crocodiles in jaded swamps.
Father took a razor blade,
slit the wrist of memory.
Drowned kittens of the balking dream
before they had a chance to claw.
Called it moving on, of course.
like prostitutes call sex a job,
then feel too much between their thighs.
Quicksand in the wishing well
demanded that he torch the house,
covet ash in urns of awkward silences.

§ § §

*Janet Buck is a three-time Pushcart Nominee and the
author of four collections PoetryBay, Artemis, The
Montserrat Review, Recursive Angel, The Carriage
House Review, Southern Ocean Review, Gertrude, and
The Pittsburgh Quarterly. For links to more of her
work,
see:http://members.aol.com/jbuck22874/whatsnew.ht
mlof poetry.*

DECEMBER   ·

by Andrew Nicoll

In the winter when the trees were bare
And the views across the river, clear,
She came to me from southern places,
Redolent of lavender and bright,
Italian lemon groves,
And Ancient Grecian ancestors,
Or Mycenaen priestesses,
Offering me handfuls of her,
Round, warm fruit tipped with blossom,
That hardened to cherry-stones,
In my mouth.
To grant me liberty,
She made herself a hostage,
And bound herself to make me free.
The pillars of her bed were olive trees
And vine leaves dappled shadows on her skin.
Between the milky moons she proffered me,
Lay all the ancient history of love.
She had the gift to heal a wounded tiger
With kisses gentle as a dove.

§ § §

Andrew is 40 years old, married with three children. He lives by the sea in Dundee, Scotland, right on the beach, close by the castle. This is his first published poem.

FOLLOWING YOUR DEPARTURE From The Physical

by David Miller

On nights like these I have only my wintry
fingers, broken cuticles, dried nubs chapped
from bleaching away tobacco stains.
Maybe they're happenstance's dingy
tomes, dry nibs that make scratching
sounds in the night as they move mechanically
across pages filled with poems. Still,
I am satisfied with this simple avodah.

I've heard the whispers already, observed
the awkward glances during Kaddish
since your recent plunge into the mystery
of silence. For years we watched you wobble
on the ledge of ecstasy - a flame leaping
from the wick, time and again pulled
back to this lower chamber. Forgive us
if your death was not a surprise.

We watched you steadily withdraw
from the palpitations of untidy rigors
and the mysterious strangers who for years
had been your verdant inspiration.
We witnessed the intensity of your prayers
and listened to the heated complaint
of a claustrophobic soul that counted the Omer
with a fire that engulfed each midot.

As for me: I am not yet finished with this husk.
Each day I rattle locked gaits with my tefilla
and refuse to turn back from iron doors. So what
if I receive only silence. There are hungry poets
who eat the challah of my table and depart
with the tzadaka of encouragement. For now
I am satisfied with this corporal shell,
though ink-smudged and gnawed upon by years.

§ § §

*David Miller has been writing poetry for more than 30
years. His work has most recently appeared in the
anthology, Poets Open Forum @ The Little Professor
Book Company in Fort Wayne, Volume II (available
through Little Professor Book Company) and in his
chapbook, Scrapbook Memories published in 2000 by
Harvest Art Press.*

*David was the founder of Harvest Art Productions which
operated poetry related events in the Portland, Oregon area
for several years, along with a tidy small press and e-zine
harvest-art.com, now owned by Mark Leair. David is a full
time student of Yeshiva Ohr HaGan in Portland, OR.*

WHAT CAME LAST

by Idra Novey

All you brought that Sunday:
the end of an absence
and a face wrung dry.
The aunts marched their troops in
talking of remorse and reunion
while their minds went on rubbing the blisters
of all they blamed you for. A decade
since you'd answered the phone.

You rose from the table
and our eyes were drawn up--
a tent of attention.
You spoke of your dead
father and the fine wool trousers
he'd bought you, paying it off
in nickels over six years.
Russian immigrants would be clothed
now in his name. Your savings
had gone to Israel.

The tent collapsed, the aunts
turned again to each other
to make sense of you.
The waitress came and filled our empty glasses.

§ § §

*Idra Novey currently teaches at the University of Chile
in Valparaiso and is coordinating an anthology of
essays by Chilean women writers for a North American
press.*

*Her poetry has appeared most recently in Cimarron
Review, Antietum Review, and Disquieting Muses, and
was included in an anthology of Chilean poetry
published by one of Chile´s central universities last
year.*

PHOTO ESSAY

DAY LILIES

BY Joan Coleman

Joan Coleman is a native New Yorker who in mind, if not in body, has never left that city. She loves black and white photography -- especially the photographs of Alfred Stieglitz and the painting and etchings of John Sloan.

ESSAY WITH PHOTOGRAPHS

THOMAS AND FROST at Dymock - August 1914

by Andrew Harold Morton

Figure 1 The Malvern Hills from the Ledbury Road

At last the summer has arrived in England. It's late July and I've just made a pilgrimage I've been meaning to get around to for years, to a spectacularly beautiful corner of England west of the Malvern Hills, just thirty miles from where I live. It is an ancient landscape substantially fashioned by Saxon earls over a thousand years ago during a period when the English were consolidating their victories against the Danes. Looking at old maps, you realise that virtually nothing has changed in the landscape although the pattern of agriculture has changed since Robert Frost and Edward Thomas spent a summer there in 1914. At that time, the main produce was fruit, pears for perry and apples for cider, as well as blackberries for dyes, and, rather charmingly, wild daffodils, which were picked by itinerant workers and exported to London by train. Nowadays, it is more conventional arable and dairy farming but though Frost lamented the dire condition of the English agricultural class, he must have felt at home among the cider apples.

In the summer of 1914, on the eve of the declaration of war, Helen Thomas, the future poet's wife, his three children, a dog called Rags and a little Russian boy who was lodging with the Thomases made a long and tedious journey from Hampshire to the hamlet of Leddington, near Dymock in Gloucestershire. It was the day after war broke out and the transport system was chaotic; on the last leg of their journey, an overzealous local policeman in the grip of spy fever challenged the suspicious strangers. When Robert Frost's name was mentioned to allay his fears, things got worse, because Frost himself was already under suspicion. Ledbury was not used to people who stayed up after 10 o'clock, had foreign accents and tramped around the countryside making notes. This, from Helen Thomas's account in *World Without End,* was the tense beginning to an historic month for English poetry.

Edward Thomas was already there, having made three visits to his friend Robert Frost in the previous few months. Thomas was ground down by over-production and, in a letter to the poet Eleanor Farjeon, can scarcely hide his excitement at the prospect of this holiday; it would last barely a month but would be instrumental in transforming Thomas from a tired hack to a poet of the first order. In the previous fifteen years, he had produced approximately two million words of travel books, biographies, one novel and countless literary reviews. He lived permanently on the edge of a nervous breakdown, a loving and devoted family man who was nevertheless permanently wracked with anxiety about where the next commission was coming from. Apart from some schoolboy efforts and one attempt at pastiche, he had not written a line of poetry, but the events of the next month, particularly the time spent with Robert Frost "in the shade of a tree smoking and talking endlessly of literature and poetry in particular" were instrumental in transforming him into a poet of lasting interest.

This is the way Little Iddens looks today -somewhat gentrified as befits its £300,000 price tag. The beech hedge which Frost admired is still there, as is the slate roof which disappointed Elinor Frost, who desperately wanted to live under thatch. Little Iddens was by no means an idyll for the Frost family. Robert continually complained about the ramshackle nature of the place to the landlord and eventually had to move out in the winter of 1914 to live with the Abercrombies at The Gallows, where Elinor eventually realised her dream.

Already living close by were Lascelles Abercrombie and Wilfrid Gibson, names now hardly known at all, who were the founding members of the Dymock poet's colony; John Drinkwater, playwright, critic and poet was often in evidence; their poetry is now mainly of historical interest, but the other three, Rupert Brooke, Robert Frost and Edward Thomas have a significant place in posterity. From the post office in Dymock, Abercrombie, Gibson, Drinkwater and Brooke (Frost, being American was excluded) posted the poems which made up New Numbers, a poetry magazine only running to four issues, but which made a massive impression on the English literary scene of the day. The poetry itself, self- styled "Georgian", typified by rural themes, sometimes with a dash of social realism, now seems rather conservative to us, but a closer inspection reveals the ache of modernism and a desire to sweep away the aesthetic triviality of late Victorian poetry. It is not the modernism of Pound, Eliot or Yeats, with their strident cultural pronouncements, because it is nearly always personal in nature. Poets like de la Mer and Masefield, both highly influential and successful at this time, delighted in the poetry making aesthetic for its own sake, but the Dymock poets are characterised by an uneasy questing after something more. Superficially, there is something Wordsworthian about them, but you don't have to dig far beneath the surface to discover a typically 20th century preoccupations with self, identity, and uncertainty. It has a lot in common with the poetry of Hardy who was often anthologised alongside them. While it never attains the monumental qualities of Yeats, Pound, and Eliot, it is arguable that its personal lyricism is more in keeping with our tastes today. The Dymock poets may be conservative with a small c, sometimes a little treacly and idealistic, but at least they did not flirt with fascism or fall in line with any other kind of cold political ideology. For a time, at least, the Georgians and the coterie surrounding Ezra Pound shared some of the same aims and sensibilities.

Frost and Thomas had met a few times in London and Leddington (which has, incidentally, three alternative spellings) before Thomas's perceptive and sympathetic reviews of *North of Boston* -- three in all -- which were published in July and August 1914. Thomas managed intuitively to get to the heart of Frost's great achievement, and in subsequent discussions, the poet and the prose writer discovered that they shared the same ideas about poetics, mainly in the need to eschew "poetic" diction and use the rhythms of ordinary speech. Frost's idea of "the sound of sense" - the idea that natural sentence rhythms are the template for real poetry was one that Thomas shared, even warning Frost to put something in writing on the subject before he did. During the month of August when the Frost and Thomas families lived a few hundred yards from each other across a couple of meadows, Frost took the

diffident Thomas in hand, and reading back to him some of his own sentences from his recently published *In Pursuit of Spring*, showed him that he was already effectively writing poetry. Frost realised that Thomas only needed to pare down his lyrical prose work to uncover the rhythms and themes of real poetry and his contribution was to give focus and direction to Thomas's work. It is clear from the correspondence between the two that Thomas was already anticipating a possible move to poetry, and hoped that Frost could help him. As Thomas's market for travel books and reviews dried up in the early months of the war, he started to produce his first poems, which he tentatively mailed to Frost. He was able to say in December 1914: "I find myself engrossed and conscious of a possible perfection as I never was in prose...I have been rather pleased with some of the pieces...Still I won't begin thanking you yet, though if you like I will put it down now that you are the only begetter right enough."
An intense correspondence continued between the men until Thomas's death serving as an artillery officer at Arras, where, one or two days before his death, he was able to read the *Times'*review of his first book of poetry which said "He is a real poet, he has the truth in him." In less than two years, he had produced roughly 140 poems of the highest quality and for once and at last his prolific quality served him well.

In 1914, Frost, aged 38, is in the ascendant at last; his first two books, *A Boy's Will* and *North of Boston*, have been published and glowingly reviewed (among others by Thomas) in London; news of his success will shortly cross the Atlantic, and he will return home to some degree of security in his career. He's a good talker, witty and engaging. He is also something of a curmudgeon, who likes the thrill of argument, conflict and even physical danger. In short, he's up for anything, seeing off gamekeepers, remonstrating with his landlord and quoting from Shakespeare over the hopeless dilapidation of Little Iddens, and even threatening to shoot the interfering local bobby who suspected, from his foreign speech, that he was a spy. Like Thomas, however, he inhabits the paradoxical states of family man and loner. He has known his share of tragedy, and, like Thomas has threatened suicide, particularly in the hilarious "dismal swamp" episode. (Both men owned an occasionally produced revolvers nd thereatened to use them on themselves.) However, Frost has a strong repressed romantic side, which emerges clearly in his Dymock poems -- *Iris by Night* is a good example. Like the lines on his face, he is clearly defined if not without his contradictions.

Figure 2 The slopes where Frost and Thomas saw the lunar halo in "Iris by Night".
In the foreground is the ancient iron age fort known as The British Camp, and in the distance the highst point of the Malvern Hills, rising to over a thousand feet.

Here are the closing lines of "Iris by Night".

"Then a small rainbow like a trellis gate,
A very small moon-made prismatic bow,
Stood closely over us through which to go.
And then we were vouchsafed the miracle
That never yet to other two befell
And I alone of us have lived to tell.
A wonder! Bow and rainbow as it bent,
Instead of moving with us as we went
(To keep the pots of gold from being found),
It lifted from its dewy pediment
Its two mote-swimming many-colored ends
And gathered them together in a ring.
And we stood in it softly circled round
From all division time or foe can bring
In a relation of elected friends."

All contemporary accounts of Thomas stress his
charisma. As Abercrombie's wife, Catherine says, "I
think Edward was the most beautiful person I have ever
seen. It was quite a shock on first meeting him unless
one had been warned." Admittedly, the Dymock people
were not prone to understatement, but pictures of him
at this age, 35, show him tall, well built, with handsome
aquiline features and a thick shock of fair hair. He looks
a little like the young Richard Burton whose Welsh
ancestry he shared. Whereas Frost is on the way up,
Thomas is in the mire. For fifteen years he has shown
classic symptoms of depression, on at least one
occasion taking his revolver out and threatening to
shoot himself. He is diffident and, he feels, a physical
coward, a conviction that is to continue to haunt him
and may have something to do with his unnecessary
decision to volunteer for active service in 1916, a

decision which leads to his death at Arras. He is also very unsure of himself and his own identity, full of regret when he is decisive, and regretting it when he is not decisive. Thomas is as undefined and as indefinite as Frost is defined and adamant. Yet all accounts of him present him as reserved in speech, yet indisputably charismatic and loveable. He is an excellent listener to Frost's good talker.

However, it is only fair to say that there are striking comparisons between the two men -- their age, for a start and the frustration experienced in their lives as writers. Both have a natural leaning towards landscape and rural themes, with a strong feeling for the inhabitants of those landscapes. They both are family men who experienced difficulties in their marital relationships, both often speaking of a sense of inadequacy in reciprocating love of devoted wives.

One incident that occurred during this period underlines that contrast. While walking one day near Abercrombie's house, Frost and Thomas are challenged by a gamekeeper brandishing a shotgun, who points that they have no right to be walking there. Frost is typically pugnacious, and later goes round to threaten the gamekeeper, an action that nearly leads to his arrest; Thomas is conciliatory and backs down, perhaps through cowardice, perhaps because he knows the rules of the English countryside better. Whatever the reason, it becomes an incident that caused him shame, and it has been suggested that Thomas volunteered for active service to exorcise the specific memory of this incident. In a revealing letter to Frost from The Front, Thomas alludes to the gamekeeper incident when he tells Frost that he had not the nerve to climb an old chimney being used as a look-out post.

Wilfrid (sic.) Gibson is a poet now only to be found lurking in obscure anthologies, but in his poem *The*

Golden Room, (1927) he presents us with an account of a meeting at his house, "The Old Nailshop," just north of Dymock, at which Frost, Thomas, Abercrombie and Brooke were present. On a summer evening, as the lamp sets the room aglow, Frost holds everyone spellbound with his witty talk, as Thomas makes the occasional dry aside and Brooke interjects his own humorous comments.

> "We talked and laughed; but, for the most part, listened
> While Robert Frost kept on and on and on,
> In his slow New England fashion, for our delight
> Holding us with shrewd turns and racy quips
> And the rare twinkle of his grave blue eyes...
>
> ...a quick flash from Abercrombie now,
> A murmured half dry aside from Thomas;
> Now a clear and laughing word from Brooke; and then
> Again Frost's rich and ripe philosophy
> That had the body and tang of good draught cider
> And poured as clear as a stream."

Figure 3 Wilfrid Gibson's The Old Nailshop -- location of "The Golden Room " -- much as it was. Gibson at the time was a successful and

highly anthologised poet on both sides of the Atlantic. His success may have occasioned some of the friction between him and Frost and Thomas, who had him down as something of a misery.

Eleanor Farjeon, childen's writer, poet ("Morning Has Broken") and diarist, also gives us some vivid moments from this summer, when she encamped it somewhat more style next door to Frost at the Glyn Iddens farmhouse. Among these snapshots are the hilarious formal dinner at a local farm where the whole company of poets end up legless on rough cider, Abercrombie's literary barbecues in a gypsy tent at Ryton, and Frost teaching some local schoolchildren to skim stones across the River Leadon or make javelins out of sapling trees. In the first volume of her autobiography, which is entirely dedicated to her relationship with Thomas, she also has a wonderful illustration of Frost's "sound of sense" doctrine: walking in the fields one day, Frost spots a ploughman a few hundred yards away and shouts some greeting to him; the ploughman shouts back, but only the rhythm of the words can be heard; "There you are," says Frost. " That's what I mean by the sound of sense."

The relationship between Frost and Thomas continues in letter form right up to Thomas's death at Arras in 1917. Frost held out the hope that Thomas would come and join him in New England where they would make Frost's farm the base camp for readings and lecture tours. Up to the point in 1915, when Thomas decides to enlist, he is still considering making this move. Frost clings on to the dream, but Thomas's destiny is taking him away in another direction where war will eventually allay the fears and ambiguities in his life. Thomas's death leaves Frost with an unbearable sense of loss, although, strangely Thomas's last two years were those in which he found his greatest personal and artistic fulfilment. The Thomas that Frost gently satirises in *The Road Not Taken* finally made up his mind in July 1915

when he signed up in The Artist's Rifles. Frost goes on
to achieve great success in his career but eternally
haunted by the memory of Thomas In 1920, Frost
writes to a friend: "Edward Thomas was the closest
friend I ever had, and I was the closest friend he ever
had; and this was something I didn't wait to realise after
he had died." And, to Helen Thomas, immediately after
his death in1917 he writes hopelessly, "I want to see
him to tell him something. I want to tell him, what I
think he liked to hear from me, that he was a poet."

Figure 4 The distant profile of May Hill where Thomas wrote "Words"
on his final visit to the area in 1916.

"Out of us all
That make rhymes,
Will you choose
Sometimes--
As the winds use
A crack in the wall
Or a drain,
Their joy or their pain
To whistle through--
Choose me,
You English words?"

For anyone trying to get onto Thomas's slightly elusive wavelength, English music of the period gives an unmistakable cue. It is also remarkable that this corner of the country is strongly associated with several notable composers of the period: Elgar, Vaughan Williams, Holst and the tragic Ivor Gurney all hail from the immediate area. And from further afield, Frank Bridge and George Butterworth also combine glorious heat-haze of pastoralism with a disturbingly modern tonality. Like Thomas, they inhabit a world in which the old certainties and myths of Britain stand on the brink of extinction in the horrors of WW1. They make a perfect musical backdrop to Dymock.

Frost revisited Dymock twice, once in 1928 and finally in 1957. Arriving at Little Iddens in a chauffeur driven Bentley and accompanied by a small entourage including his granddaughter and a photographer, he muses on how little and how much things have changed. What exactly happened on that day is not entirely clear, but the picture of the old man with his reminiscences has great emotional resonance.

Figure 5 Frost visits Little Iddens 1957. I apologise for the lens flare

which is a result of taking this image from behind glass in St Mary's church, Dymock.

Part of the emotional pull of the Dymock experience is nostalgia for a brief golden age. I suppose that all of us have a "Golden Room" somewhere in our past - a brief interlude of emotional and spiritual perfection. Drinwater in his poem *Daffodils,* Frost in *The Thatch* (1928), Gibson in the *Golden Room*(1927), and Abercrombie in *Ryton Firs,* all hark back to Dymock with a heavy sense of nostalgia. Brooke dies in 1915 of a mosquito bite that led to septicaemia on his way to Gallipoli; Thomas from the blast of a shell at Arras; Abercrombie and Gibson never again reach the heights they did briefly on the eve of WW1 and go into gentle decline in terms of creativity, health and reputation.

For anyone interested in reading about the Dymock period, there are four books I would recommend: top of the list I would place Eleanor Farjeon's *Autobiography Volume One,* which is entirely dedicated to Thomas and contains probably the best collection of anecdotal material; for a very good brief introduction, the is Linda Hart's *Once They lived in Gloucestershire*; slightly more detailed and is Keith Clarke's *The Muse Colony,* which I would strongly recommend. Both of these books offer a degree of critical biography interspersed with the relevant poems. Also available is Sean Street's *The Dymock Poets,* which offers a fuller historical account, including the literary milieu of the time and much more on the aftermath. I confess that I have not read Andrew Motion's *Elected Friends,* but this is generally acknowledged as the major single work on Thomas's poetry. Nearly all of Thomas's prose work is out of print, and is fairly difficult to find second hand. His letters to Robert Frost, Eleanor Farjeon and Gordon Bottomley can all be read in separate volumes, although, as with his literary reviews, the output was so prodigious that it would be unreasonable to expect to find it all in one place.

Figure 6 A view from The Malverns towards Ledbury on a suitably hazy English summer's day.Even is a cyclonic period, this view over Gloucestershire and Herefordshire towards Wales has a blue misty quality to it.

Bibliography:

Edward Thomas -War Diaries
Edward Thomas -Collected Poems
Edward Thomas - In Pursuit of Spring
Eleanor Farjeon - Autobiography - Vol. One
Robert Frost - A Boy's Will, North of Boston and A Further Range
Helen Thomas et al. -Under Storm's Wing
Jeffrey Myers - Robert Frost
Linda Hart - Once They Lived In Gloucestershire
Selected Letters of Edward Thomas to Gordon Bottomley
Keith Clarke- The Muse Colony
Sean Street- The Dymock Poets

§ § §

Born in Nottingham, England, 1950, Andrew studied at Birmingham University under such figures as David Lodge, Stuart Hall, Richard Hoggart, Park Honan and Stanley Wells, graduating in English Literature and Language in 1972. He has taught English in Birmingham for twenty-six years, where he currently lives with his wife and three children.

He also has a serious sideline in music, credits including original music for several TV documentaries, as well as the scores for the groundbreaking musicals Love and Spare Parts and Utopia and Beyond.

He has also written one stage play, How Low Can You Go? and dabbles in fiction on the Zoetrope Virtual Studio website, an activity which has led to publication in several Internet magazines.

He is a founder member of the seventies jazz/rock outfit Slender Loris, and has spent the last few months making their music available through mp3.comand constructing a Slender Loris website.

MID MONTH SURPRISE

SONNETS

BY Richard Jackson

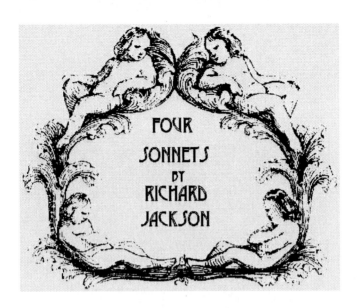

FOUR
SONNETS
BY
RICHARD
JACKSON

MORNING SONG

I think it is her step that brushes the dew from the grass,
a step like some sort of goddess, maybe Diana opening
flowers, opening the morning sky, her presence reviving
the glow that slept all night in the lake like the moonlight's mast.
Love is what entangles the heart, breaks the soul like glass,
follows her step like some hunter-- it's not her he's stalking
but whoever sees her, whoever opens his eyes to this morning,
to this light that falls like rain turning other desires to ash.
It's her walking that shows us where to go, her words
that tell us what to say, her wayward glance that tells us
what to watch, her gestures that tell us where to touch.
It's these four things that make a myth of every dusk--
I think I have become some sort of modern Tantalus,
I think I have become lost in the sun like a nightbird.

LOVE'S CONTRARIES

Peace-- I can't find it, but I'm not about to wage any war--
I fear the air that fills my words with hope, I burn in their ice,
I rise like smoke and grasp at a sky wrinkled with stars,
but the cosmos is a collapsed lung -- there's nothing left to embrace.
Love is the senile jailer who neither opens nor locks the door,
who can't think of a way to torture me, or a way to cut the noose,
doesn't send assassins or come himself, but doesn't cut the bars,--
maybe he wants me displayed at market like a wild-eyed fish on ice.
I see with a stone for an eye and shout with a voice full of chaff,
I want to leap from a roof, yet Love coaxes me from his cliffs--
I hate what I've become, but love you dearly, like nobody else.
I live on pain instead of bread, and use my tears to laugh,
I despise, with equal opportunity, both death and life--
all because of you my dear, I enter this heaven, this hell.

THE HUNT

Those sweet hills where I left the self that I will be and always was,
that self I left encased in a waterfall which hangs like a frozen sleeve,
those hills whose memory hunts me as I hunt it, where I grieve
and delight in this burden that has become my life's cause--
those hills, that maze, where I find myself in eternity's pause,
where every path I cross is the same path, where to love is to believe
that the beautiful yoke of these hills and self can never be relieved,
those sweet hills-- no matter how far I go the closer to them I draw.
I'm like one of those gutted deer hunted in myth or in reality,
it's all the same now, that the hunter drags from the forest in a cart,
that froze momentarily on a ridge, heard the hunter's aim, unable to flee,
and crashed wildly then through the underbrush of the heart,
arrow hanging from its side, but almost thankful for the pure bounty
it offers, tired with its pain, tired of living so long and so far apart.

THE PAUSE

Let's stop time, Love, to see what those clouds yearn
to be, to listen to that butterfly stir the air around us,
to hear, at dusk, the stars begin like crickets, tremulous,
or feel their light begin to ripple in the lowest ferns;
let's see how skillfully the night covers this field of moons,
the way your own own look has passed the sentries of my heart,--
let's add some message twig to this nest we'd set so far apart
we only spoke with words that waited all winter in their cocoons.
Not long ago my sky was full of razors, the wind
had pried the roots of hope-- now every mountain dreams
to hold your step, every tree has begged to give you shade,--
the whole sky wakes like struck flint, a hawk reinvents the wind,
the huge valleys of the flower open their unimaginable scenes,
every clock drowns in your eyes for this world that will not fade.

§§§

RICHARD JACKSON is the author of five books of poems, most recently *Heartwall* (UMass, Juniper Prize '00), *Alive All Day* (Cleveland State Prize, '92), a Selected Poems in Slovene, and the forthcoming *Unauthorized Autobiography: New and Selected Poems* (Ashland University Poetry Press, 2003).

He has also published four chapbooks adaptations from Petrarch and other Italian poets (Black Dirt Press) and a limited edition of Petrarchan poems (Aureole Press,Univ. of Toledo). His own poems have been translated into a dozen languages. He has edited two anthologies of Slovene poetry: *The Fire Under the Moon* (Black Dirt, '99) and *Four Slovenian Poets* (Aleph, '93) and edits an eastern European Chapbook series and two journals, *Poetry Miscellany* and *mala revija*. He is also the author of a book of criticism, *Dismantling Time in Contemporary American Poetry* (winner of the Agee Prize), and *Acts of Mind: Interviews With Contemporary American Poets* (winner of Choice Award).

He has been a member of the Sarajevo Committee organized by P.E.N. Int'l and has worked with various groups concerning the Balkan wars and fund raising for refugees. In 2000 he was awarded the Order of Freedom Medal for literary and humanitarian work in the Balkans by the President of Slovenia. He has received Guggenheim NEA, NEH, and 2 Witter-Bynner Fellowships, a Prairie Schooner reader's Choice Award, and the Crazyhorse prize, and is the winner of four Pushcart Prizes and appeared in *Best American Poems 1997* and several other anthologies, and his poems have appeared on the internet in Poetry Daily and Verse Daily. He has been a Fulbright Exchange poet to former Yugoslavia and returns each year with groups of students. He teaches at UT-Chattanooga where he directs the Meacham Writers' Conference and at Vermont College's MFA program, winning teaching awards at both schools.

STAFF

On the first anniversary of Literary Potpourri, we would like to again extend thanks to our talented associates, the people whose vision and dedication made it all possible:

William Coleman
Mary McCluskey
David Hubert
Diana Butcher
Shaula Evans

393

INDEX BY AUTHOR

394